The Godly Woman

Personal Bible Studies
for the
Christian Woman

Irma Warr

Foreword by Charlie Riggs

Creative Resources

Waco, Texas

Workbook
THE GODLY WOMAN

Acknowledgements

My Special Thanks

—To my husband, Gene, who did *so much* of the research work and constantly counseled and encouraged me along the way . . . and whose love keeps me going.

—To my three sons—my treasures—Kevin, Kyle, and Kory who often gave me those "diversions" every writer *needs* in the middle of a thought (to make a peanut butter sandwich, or change a diaper, or hear a story, or kiss a hurt)! . . . and without whom the chapters on being a mother could not have been written.

—To those who have typed and proofread the manuscripts, and the girls who helped in our home to allow me to have time to write.

—To the men in my husband's Bible Study who did so much of the original research work and helped greatly by prayer.

—To the girls in my Bible Study who helped so much through prayer, research, encouragement, checking and proofreading manuscripts, etc.

> To *All* of these
> this book is
> lovingly dedicated

Contents

Foreword

Today, perhaps more than at any time in history, multitudes are involved in personal Bible study and prayer, individually and with fellowship groups. A tremendous spiritual hunger is being mct by a variety of good study materials that are currently available.

Personally, I believe that *The Godly Woman: Personal Bible Studies for the Christian Woman* is unique. In this book, you have an excellent combination of well-designed lessons with relevance to thc issues and problems of the day, deeply rooted in Scripture with practical application of biblical truth to specific areas of life. You also have a large variety of rich resource material in the "Suggestions for Further Study" section at the end of each session.

If you use the study in a group setting, another unique feature you have is a "built-in" fellowship through prayer and sharing. Group members pray for each other daily, and in weekly Bible discussion share their Bible discoveries and what God is doing in their lives.

I am confident that any person who is willing to follow the disciplines set forth in these studies will greatly enhance her relationship to God and man and her effectiveness as a Christian witness.

Charlie Riggs
Counselor Training and Followup
The Billy Graham Evangelistic
Association

About *The Godly Woman* Bible Study

Purpose
To help produce in you the kind of person whose life is explainable only in terms of God. To create in you the kind of life other women seek for help and counsel. To enable you to more perfectly reflect the Lord Jesus Christ in his glory.

Design
The Godly Woman Bible study is designed for individual or group use.

1. This book, *The Godly Woman: Personal Bible Studies for the Christian Woman*, contains twenty-two sessions you can work through at your own pace and in the privacy of your personal study time. It is meant to be written in. You would need no further materials unless you desired to do the additional study recommended at the close of each session.

2. This workbook is also part of a complete program for groups utilizing a Teacher's Guide and four 90-minute cassette tapes. It is designed to be covered in twenty-two, 1 hour sessions and contains everything you would need to conduct an effective group study.

Suggestions For Further Study
At the end of each chapter you will find "Suggestions for Further Study." The books and pamphlets may be obtained from your local Christian bookstore. The tapes are available on a loan basis (no charge except for postage and handling) from:

> The Discipleship Library
> 435 West Boyd
> Norman, Oklahoma 73069

Follow-Up

The Godly Woman Bible Study is the companion program for *The. Godly Man* course. Both are available with *Personal Bible Studies* workbooks for individual study and a Leader's kit for group use. For information concerning these and over fifty additional group study programs available through Creative Resources, write P.O. Box 1790, Waco, Texas 76703 or call toll free 1–800–433–2380. A no-obligation thirty-day review program is available upon request.

THE
GODLY
WOMAN AS A
DISCIPLE

CHAPTER I
THE FOUNDATION OF A DISCIPLE

The Foundation of a Disciple.
"For other foundation can no man lay than that is laid, which is Jesus Christ." I Cor. 3:11

I. Who Jesus Christ is:
  A. He is God.
    1. Jesus Claimed:
      a. Matthew 28:18

      . . . .
      . . . .

      b. Matthew 9:6

      . . . .
      . . . .

      c. John 14:9

      . . . .
      . . . .

      d. John 10:30

      . . . .
      . . . .

      e. John 15:21

      . . . .
      . . . .

      f. John 10:10

      . . . .
      . . . .

    2. The Bible says He:
      a. John 8:58, Col. 1:17

      . . . .
      . . . .

      b. Col. 1:16

      . . . .
      . . . .

B. He is a perfect man.
   3. Match the following human characteristics of Jesus
      with the verses:

   weary _____   John 4:6
   hungry _____   Matt. 4:2
   sleepy _____   Mark 4:38
   sorrowful _____   John 11:35
   tempted _____   Heb. 4:15

II What Jesus did.
    4. Why did He come? Luke 19:10

       . . . .
       . . . .

    5. Romans 5:8 says that God showed His love for us by

       . . . .
       . . . .

    6. Who needs Jesus to die for him? . . . .
       Why is this true? Express Romans 6:23 in your own
       words . . . .
       . . . .
       . . . .
    7. What did Christ do on the cross? I Peter 2:24 . . . .
       . . . .
    8. What sign did Jesus say He would give the Jews?
       John 2:18-22 . . . .
       . . . .
       . . . .
    9. What sign did Jesus give? Luke 24:1-7 . . . .
       . . . .
       . . . .

"God is on one side and all the people on the other side, and Christ Jesus, Himself man, is between them to bring them together."
I Timothy 2:5 Living Bible

—4—

III. What the life, death, and resurrection of Jesus means.

    10. Man is separated from God by sin. According to Jesus Christ, what ways are available to man by which he may return to God? John 14:6

. . . .

. . . .

. . . .

. . . .

    11. Who does God want in fellowship with Himself? I Tim. 2:4, II Peter 3:9. . . . .

. . . .

    12. Why are some people still not in fellowship with God? John 3:18 . . . .

. . . .

. . . .

    13. What is the condition of those who have not believed Jesus? John 3:36 . . . .

. . . .

. . . .

    14. When a person realizes that he is separated from God because of his sin, what should his response be? Luke 13:3 . . . .

. . . .

. . . .

". . . Except ye repent, ye shall all likewise perish." Luke 13:3

    15. What does it mean to repent? Matt. 3:2-8 . . . .

. . . .

. . . .

    16. According to I John 5:11, 12, who has eternal life? (fellowship with God) . . . .

. . . .

17. In the light of John 1:12, 13, and Eph. 2:8, 9, those who have eternal life (fellowship with God) and will be in heaven, are those who:

True   False
( )   ( ) Do more good things than bad during their lifetime.
( )   ( ) Repent of their sins.
( )   ( ) Live as good as some church members.
( )   ( ) Clean up their lives so as to be acceptable with God.
( )   ( ) Receive Jesus Christ.
( )   ( ) Join a church and are baptized.
( )   ( ) Are sincere.
( )   ( ) Really believe in something.

18. In your opinion, what must one do in order to be in fellowship with God and have eternal life? . . . .

. . . .
. . . .
. . . .
. . . .
. . . .

19. Do you have eternal life? . . . .
20. How do you know? (125 words or less) . . . .

. . . .
. . . .
. . . .
. . . .
. . . .
. . . .
. . . .
. . . .
. . . .
. . . .

Suggestions For Further Study
Tape No. BSU 77a — "Discipleship"

CHAPTER II

GOD'S PROVISION FOR A DISCIPLE

I. The source of God's provision is His grace. Grace has been defined as "the unmerited favor of God." Or, as
God's
Riches
At
Christ's
Expense

Grace is God doing for us what we in no way deserve. Mercy is God not doing to us what we so richly deserve.

1. Why did Paul say he was the man he was? I Cor. 15:10

. . . .

. . . .

2. To whom will God be gracious? Exodus 33:19 . . . .

. . . .

3. Why did God choose Israel as His special people? Deut. 7:7-8 . . . .

. . . .

4. If we try to earn God's favor in any way, what does this do to His grace? Gal. 2:21 . . . .

. . . .

II. The channel of grace.

5. How do we receive the grace of God? John 1:17 . . . .

. . . .

. . . .

6. According to Romans 3:24, we are justified (declared "not guilty" and made right with God) by . . . . , through . . . .

. . . .

7. **What is another result of the grace of God? Eph. 2:7**

. . . .

8. Eph. 2:8 teaches us that we are saved through . . . . and that it is the . . . . of God.

—7—

9. The grace of God comes to those who believe through Jesus Christ. According to the following scriptures, what good things come to us through Jesus Christ?

Col. 2:9-10 ....

....

Eph. 1:3 ....

....

1 Cor. 1:30 ....

....

....

....

I Cor. 1:4-5 ....

Phil. 4:13 ....

III. The means of grace.

10. Our access to the grace of God as given through Jesus Christ is by .... Romans 5:1-2.

11. What are the three time elements in regard to our faith? II Cor. 1:10 ....

....

Romans 5:9-10 teaches that we have been saved from the penalty of sin (past), are being delivered from the power of sin (present) and will ultimately be freed from the presence of sin (future). Past FAITH is that which we exercised when we received Jesus Christ. Future FAITH is the looking forward to being with Him in heaven. Present FAITH is believing and trusting Him for each day's problems now.

12. Col. 2:6 says we should walk in the same way we received Christ. We received Him (became children of God) by ....

....

(Gal. 3:26)

....

(Rom. 1:17)

....

Col. 2:6 in the Living Bible says "and now just as you trusted Christ to save you, trust Him, too, for each day's problems; live in vital union with Him."

13. **Self effort is the opposite of faith. What area of your life are you still trying to handle by your own effort and worry, instead of trusting Jesus Christ?** . . . .

. . . .

. . . .

14. What will you do this coming week to bring faith into operation in this area, so that you may experience the grace of God? (Express it in personal terms using the pronoun me, my, and mine) . . . .

. . . .

. . . .

IV. The results of grace.

15. What is God's will for every born-again believer? Romans 8:29 . . . .

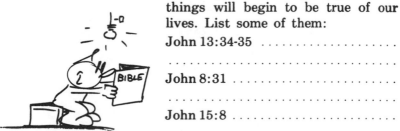

. . . .

Eph. 4:13 . . . .

. . . .

16. What are we commanded to do? . . . . . II Peter 3:18 . . . .

. . . .

. . . .

Much of the balance of this study booklet will deal with the "how to" of growing in the grace and knowledge of Jesus and becoming more and more like Him. You are embarking on the world's most exciting adventure.

17. As we grow in discipleship, certain things will begin to be true of our lives. List some of them:

John 13:34-35 . . . .

. . . .

John 8:31 . . . .

. . . .

John 15:8 . . . .

. . . .

Acts 6:7 . . . .

18. Which of these areas do you feel you need the most help in at this time? . . . .
. . . .

19. What will you do this next week to allow God to minister His grace to you in this area? (Be specific — don't deal in generalities) . . . .
. . . .
. . . .
. . . .

Suggestions For Further Study

Tape 1272 A, B — "Grace of God"

The Attributes of God by Arthur W. Pink, Reiner Publications.

The Saving Life of Christ by Major W. Ian Thomas, Zondervan Publishing House.

CHAPTER III

THE CHRIST-CENTERED LIFE
[THE WHEEL]

(Used by permission of The Navigators)

The key to living a victorious, Spirit-filled Christian life is Jesus Christ as the Center and Lord of all we do. With Christ in control, life is balanced and effective. The Wheel illustrates this Christ-centered life.

WHEEL EXPLANATION

- Just as the driving force in a wheel comes from the hub; so the power to live the Christian life comes from Jesus Christ the Center. He lives in us in the Person of the Holy Spirit, whose expressed purpose is to glorify Christ. The rim represents the Christian responding to Christ's Lordship through whole-hearted, day-by-day obedience to Him.

- **The spokes show the means by which Christ's power becomes operative in our lives. We maintain personal contact with God through the vertical spokes — the Word and prayer. The Word is our spiritual food as well as our sword for spiritual battle. It is the foundational spoke for effective Christian living.**

- Opposite this is the spoke representing **Prayer**. Through prayer we have direct communication with our heavenly Father and receive provision for our needs. As we pray we show our dependence upon and trust in Him.

- The horizontal spokes concern our relationship to people — believers, through Christian fellowship; and unbelievers, through witnessing. **Fellowship** centered around the Lord Jesus Christ provides the mutual encouragement, admonition and stimulation we all need.

- The first three spokes prepare us for passing on to others all that we have received from the Lord. This is accomplished through **Witnessing**, sharing our own experience of Christ and declaring and explaining the Gospel, God's power to save.

PART 1 — THE HUB AND THE RIM

I. Christ the Hub.
    1. Why should Christ be the center of the believer's life?
       John 13:13 . . . .
       I Cor. 7:23 . . . .
       Heb. 13:8 . . . .
       I Peter 5:7 . . . .
    2. In your opinion, what are some of the substitutions people make for Christ in the center of their lives? . . . . .

      . . . .
      . . . .
      . . . .
      . . . .

II. The Rim.
    1. How will others judge our relationship to Jesus Christ?
       Matt. 7:15-20. . . . .

      . . . .
      . . . .

    2. Our obedience indicates:
       John 14:15 . . . .
       John 15:14 . . . .
       Matt. 7:21 . . . .
       I John 2:3-5 . . . .
    3. What are some things God promises those who obey Him?
       Deut. 28:2 . . . .
       Ex. 19:5 . . . .
       I Peter 1:22 . . . .
    4. What are we to obey? John 14:21, Joshua 22:5 . . . .

      . . . .
    5. What are the two greatest commandments? Luke 10:27

      . . . .
      . . . .

6. I Sam. 15:22 teaches us that obedience is better than . .
.... There is no
substitute for obedience in the Christian life.

7. List three "sacrifices" that people try to substitute for
obedience today: ....
....
....

8. Express Romans 8:32 in your own words. ....
....
....
....

9. In the light of Romans 8:32
   A. What has God given us?.......................
   B. What will He give us? ....

10. Why does God want us to obey Him? Jeremiah 29:11 . .
....
Ephesians 1:8 in the Living Bible says "And He has
showered down upon us the riches of His grace—for
how well he understands us and knows what is best
for us at all times."

11. Do you believe God knows what is best for you and
wants the best for you? ....

12. Then why would you not obey Him? ....
....
....
....

13. Obedience is a matter of the .... Deut. 5:29

PART 2 — THE VERTICAL INTAKE SPOKES

III. The Word.
    1. Why do you believe what you believe? Or, asking it
       another way, what is the basis of your final authority
       for what you believe?

                (Check One)

      A.   It seems reasonable to me.
      B.   I feel that way about it.
      C.   My own experience.
      D.   The experience of others.
      E.   My church tells me.
      F.   My parents taught me.
      G.   The Bible.
      H.   The sacred writings of the ages.

WHERE IS THE BLUEPRINT

    2. In II Tim. 3:16, what does the Bible say about
      A. It's origin? . . . .

        . . . .

      B. It's profit in:
        1) . . . . (what to believe and do)
        2) . . . . (when we get off the road)
        3) . . . . (how to get back on the road)
        4) . . . . (how to stay on the road)
    3. List opposite the scriptures below some further claims
      of the Bible:

        II Tim. 3:15 . . . .
        I Peter 2:2 . . . .
        Ps. 119:105 . . . .
        John 15:3 . . . .
        Ps. 119:165 . . . .
        Romans 10:17 . . . .

BIBLE

The Word of God is MATCHLESS — Man cannot duplicate it.

The Word of God is ULTIMATE — it is final, it will not be changed, there is no appeal, John 12:48.

The Word of God is PERFECT — how would you improve on John 3:16?

The Word of God is TIMELESS — The Bible works now and forever.

The Word of God is INDESTRUCTABLE — Man cannot destroy it. Luke 21:33.

Whenever the Word of God is ineffective in a life, it is for one of three reasons:
1. Neglect
2. Doubt
3. Disobedience

IV. Prayer.
    1. Define prayer . . . .
    2. What are two reasons why we miss much of what God has for us?
       A. James 4:2 . . . .

      . . . .
       B. James 4:3 . . . .

    . . . .
    3. Prayer is an act of faith. How should we pray?
      Matthew 21:22 . . . .
    4. Since God knows our needs (Matt. 6:8), why should we bring them before Him?
      (MATCH THE PHRASES WITH THE VERSES)
      Luke 18:1 ( )   1. So our joy might be complete

      John 16:24 ( )   2. It is commanded.
      Ps. 62:8   ( )   3. To experience His peace.
      Phil. 4:6, 7 ( )   4. To demonstrate trust in Him
    5. What do you feel Matthew 7:7 teaches about prayer?

    . . . .

    . . . .

    . . . .
    6. Our God is a God of law and order. The physical laws operate in certain ways. Effects obey causes. This is true spiritually. God has placed some conditions on effective prayer. Discover and list some of them below.
      Isa. 59:1, 2 . . . .

      . . . .
      I John 3:22 . . . .

      . . . .
      I John 5:14, 15 . . . .

      . . . .
      I Peter 3:7 . . . .

7. How can we know when we are praying "according to God's will?" ....
   ....
   ....

8. What does it mean to pray "In Jesus Name?" ....
   ....
   ....

9. How can we prevent sin from hindering our prayer life? I John 1:9 ....
   ....

10. Most people have experienced the discouragement of seemingly unanswered prayers. Match up some reasons for ineffective prayer with the verses below:

    Job 35:12, 13   ( )   1. Lack of heart preparation
    Eph. 6:12   ( )   2. Pride
    Ps. 139:23, 24   ( )   3. Satan's hindering
    Matt. 6:33   ( )   4. Poor value system
    Mark 11:25, 26   ( )   5. Lack of faith
    James 1:6-8   ( )   6. Unforgiving spirit

11. We have discovered some conditions of effective prayer and some hindrances. Which two do you feel you fail in most? ....
   ....
   Why? ....
   ....
   ....
   ....
   ....
   ....

12. What will you do this week to allow God to begin correcting these in your life? (Who will you ask to check up on you next week?) ....

. . . .
. . . .
. . . .
. . . .
. . . .
. . . .
. . . .

Suggestions For Further Study

Discovering How to Pray, by Hope McDonald, Londervan
Prayer, by O'Hallesby, Augsburg Press
The Prayer Life, by Andrew Murray, Moody Press
How to Pray, by R. A. Torrey, Moody Press
Prevailing Prayer, by D. L. Moody, Moody Press

Tape 368 — "Prayer"
Tape 1246 —"Immediate Asking and Receiving"
Tape 60 — "Authority and Sufficiency of the Scriptures"
Tape 87 — "The Word of God"

PART 3 — THE HORIZONTAL OUTREACH SPOKES

V. Fellowship: Fellowship is defined as comradeship, companionship, a relation in which parties hold something in common, mutual sharing, or friendly association. Someone has said, in the Christian context, that fellowship is two fellows on the same ship going in the same direction.

1. What is the basis of Christian fellowship? I John 1:3 . . .

. . . .

. . . .

2. The fellowship of the world rests on many different bases. Name some of the things which draw people together.

. . . .

. . . .

. . . .

. . . .

. . . .

. . . .

3. Why is Christian fellowship more permanent than the world's fellowship? Hebrews 13:8 . . . .

. . . .

4. Discover and list from Acts 2:42 four things in which the early church continued.

. . . .

. . . .

5. The New English Bible translates the part of Acts 2:42 on fellowship as "sharing the common life." Explain in practical ways what the term "sharing the common life" means to you. . . . .

. . . .

. . . .

. . . .

6. Why is fellowship important to us?

Matthew 18:19-20 . . . .

Lev. 26:8 . . . .

Ecc. 4:9, 10 . . . .

Heb. 10:25 . . . .

7. Check two basic things which you feel hinder Christian fellowship most today:

Pride	( )	
Selfishness	( )	
Lack of Love	( )	
Lack of understanding	( )	
Independence	( )	
Busyness	( )	
Fear	( )	
Hyprocrisy	( )	
Sin in the life	( )	
Other . . . . ( )	

8. Do you have at least one Christian friend with whom you are able to be completely yourself, knowing she will accept you and love you anyway?

A. If so, pause now and thank God for her. Thank him for being this kind of friend this coming week.

B. If not, pause now and ask God to bring someone like this into your life.

Read the prayer of Jesus in John 17 with the intention of discovering what He revealed about the importance of fellowship.

VI. Witness

1. Whose job is it to save people? I Tim. 1:15 . . . .

2. We are simply the . . . . of Christ. II Cor. 5:19, 20

3. The power is in (Romans 1:16. Check one)

The presentation	( )
The one presenting Christ	( )
Just the right setting	( )
The Gospel	( )

4. Define "the Gospel" in your own words. I Cor. 15:3, 4 . .

. . . .

. . . .

. . . .

5. What is a personal testimony? I John 1:3, Acts 4:20 ...

. . . .

. . . .

. . . .

. . . .

. . . .

. . . .

6. Read Acts 26:4-23. This is Paul's personal testimony. From the following portions of Acts 26, match up the part of Paul's testimony which applies:

Acts 26:4-11 ( )   1. How Paul met Christ.

Acts 26:12-18 ( )   2. What life has been like since he met Christ.

Acts 26:19-23 ( )   3. What life was like before he met Christ.

7. Write out your own personal testimony in 125 words or less, including the three basic elements mentioned above.

. . . .

. . . .

. . . .

. . . .

. . . .

. . . .

. . . .

. . . .

. . . .

. . . .

. . . .

. . . .

. . . .

. . . .

. . . .

. . . .

. . . .

. . . .

8. The "Do you know the steps to peace with God" pamphlet furnished with this study is one way of presenting the Gospel. Share the pamphlet completely with someone other than your family this week.

Suggestions For Further Study

Tape 1603 — "The Wheel"

Tape 1149 — "Enemies of Evangelism"

Tape 234 — "Witnessing"

Tape 772 — "Soul-Winning; Questions and Answers on Evangelism"

Tape 34 — "Harvest of Crops"

Tape BSU-170 — "Link In The Chain"

Winning Ways, by Leroy Eims, Victor Books.

Don't Fake It . . . Say it with Love, by Howard Hendricks, Victor Books

CHAPTER IV

THE DEVOTIONAL LIFE

The devotional life is known by many names. Daily devotions, morning watch, quiet time, time with the Lord. Naming it and knowing it doesn't mean we practice it. Few people do on a consistent basis. Whatever name is used, it means a specific time daily when we let God speak to us from His Word, the Bible, and when we speak to Him in prayer. It is daily, consistent fellowship with Christ.

I. Why daily devotions?

Match the following statements with the appropriate scriptures answering the question, "why daily devotions?"

( ) Personal joy   1. I Cor. 1:9
( ) Not forget God   2. II Cor. 3:18
( ) Worship   3. Psa. 16:11
( ) Man's soul need   4. Jn. 4:24
( ) To know God   5. Jer. 2:32
( ) Part of God's call   6. Psa. 42:1, 2
( ) An invitation to us to   7. Isa. 43:10
     be like Christ   Hosea 6:3, 2B

II. Examples of daily devotions in the lives of great men of the Bible.

After the following scriptures, write down the name of a man and what he did or desired regarding his fellowship with God and in your opinion, why this was true.

Gen. 19:27 . . . .

. . . .

. . . .

Psa. 63:1, 2 . . . .

. . . .

. . . .

Psa. 27:4 . . . .

. . . .

. . . .

Ex. 33:14, 15 . . . .

. . . .

. . . .

Mark 1:35 . . . .

. . . .

Phil. 3:10 . . . .

. . . .

III Elements in the daily devotional life.
   A. Scriptures
      1. How was the king to read the scriptures according to Deut. 17:18-20? . . . .

      . . . .

      2. Why was he to read it? . . . .

      . . . .

      3. How does this apply to us today? . . . .

      . . . .

      4. Our identification with Christ is to be on a . . . .

         . . . . basis according to Luke 9:23.
   B. Prayer.
      1. When should we pray? Luke 18:1 . . . .
      2. What does I Thess. 5:17 mean? . . . .

      . . . .

      . . . .

      . . . .

      . . . .

      . . . .

      3. Effective prayer includes several elements. Match the elements with the scriptures then number them in the order that you feel they should be introduced in your own prayer time.
                        ELEMENTS
      ( ) Praise . . . . .Prov. 28:13
      ( ) Intercession (Prayer for others) . . . . .Ps. 50:23
      ( ) Petition (Prayer for myself) . . . . . . .Eph. 5:20
      ( ) Confession . . . . .I Sam. 12:23
      ( ) Thanksgiving . . . . .Phil. 4:6-7

IV. Results of daily devotions.
   1. From the following scriptures, search and discover some results of a daily devotional life.

II Tim. 3:16 . . . .

. . . .

. . . .

Joshua 1:8 . . . .

. . . .

. . . .

Hosea 6:6 (Living) "I don't want your sacrifices—I want your love ; I don't want your offerings—I want you to know Me." . . . .

. . . .

. . . .

Psa. 139:23, 24 . . . .

. . . .

. . . .

Psa. 119:105 . . . .

. . . .

. . . .

I Peter 2:2, 3 . . . .

. . . .

. . . .

I Jn. 1:7 . . . .

. . . .

. . . .

V. Hindrances to Daily Devotions.
   1. From the following scriptures, list some of the hindrances to an effective daily devotional life and what steps you would take to overcome these hindrances.

Hindrance	How I Would Overcome It
Prov. 6:9	. . . .
. . . .	. . . .
. . . .	. . . .
Rev. 3:17	. . . .
. . . .	. . . .
. . . .	. . . .

Psa. 127:2 .... | ....
.... | ....
Matt. 6:33 .... | ....
.... | ....
.... | ....
Mark 4:19 .... | ....
.... | ....
.... | ....
I Jn. 2:15, 16 ..... | ....
.... | ....
Psa. 66:18 .... | ....
.... | ....
.... |

Remember, in order to have an effective daily devotional life you need:
1. A time when you are at your best.
2. A place — quiet spot all alone.
3. A plan — some pre-determined approach.
4. A Bible — a translation you enjoy and don't mind writing in.
5. A notebook — to jot down what God says to you.
6. A prayer list — to help you remember.
7. An expectant heart — you have an audience with the King.

PRIVATE

ASSIGNMENT: Fill out the following questions, then read the passages listed on the day assigned, and answer the questions for each passage.

BY GOD'S GRACE, I WILL HAVE A DAILY DEVOTIONAL LIFE THIS WEEK. TIME ....
PLACE ....
WHICH TRANSLATION ....
LENGTH OF TIME ....

Monday — Phil. 2:5 thru 10. Make note of the steps which took Jesus to his place of exaltation. How do these steps apply to us today?

Tuesday — Col. 1:14 thru 20. Substitute the name of Christ for the personal pronoun in the passage. What new insight did you receive from this reading?

Wednesday — John 15:1 thru 17. Who is the vine? Who are the branches? What does it mean to "abide?"

Thursday — Matt. 25:31 thru 46. How does this apply today?

Friday — Hebrews 12:1 thru 6. What do you feel is necessary for us to "finish the race?"

Saturday — Acts 2:14 thru 36. What were the most important facts which Peter covered in this sermon of his?

Sunday — Psalm 145. List the things the Psalmist was praising God for.

Suggestions For Further Study

Tapes 1517A "Quiet Time" and 1404 A B "Bible Study"

Quiet Time — Inter Varsity Press

Manna in the Morning by Stephen Olford, Moody Press

My Heart Christ's Home by Robert B. Munger, Billy Graham Evangelistic Association, Box 779, Minneapolis, Minn.

Time Alone With God, Billy Graham Evangelistic Association.

7 Minutes With God, The Navigators, Colorado Springs, Colorado.

Daily Devotional Diary (a reading plan with written reproduction) The Navigators.

CHAPTER V

THE LORDSHIP OF CHRIST
[Death to the Self-Life]

I. The Bible speaks of Jesus Christ as being Lord. He wants to be Lord of every believer's life.

The word Lord means: master, governer, chief, boss, ruler, sovereign. The term lordship indicates: ownership, absolute control, authority, rule, or dominion.

  1. What right does Jesus Christ have to be Lord of our lives?

    Heb. 1:1, 2 ....

    Acts 2:36 ....

    John 13:13 ....

    I Cor. 6:20 ....

    John 15:5 ....

  2. There are certain characteristics present in a life in which Christ is the Lord. Name some of these characteristics found in the following Scriptures:

    Luke 9.23 ....

    Gal. 2:20 ....

    Rom. 1:16 ....

    Luke 6:46 ....

    Phil. 3:7, 8 ....

    John 8:31 ....

    Gal. 5:22, 23 ....

    John 13:34, 35 ....

  3. There are certain practical steps we can take to make Christ the Lord of our lives. Some are listed below: Carefully study each step and then express in your own words what you think it means in a practical way in a person's life.

    A. John 12:24, 25 — death to the self life. ....

    ....

    ....

    ....

B. Romans 8:13 and Gal. 5:16, 17. We cannot commit suicide on a cross. The Holy Spirit can mortify (crucify) the flesh (self life). . . . .

. . . .

. . . .

. . . .

C. We do have a choice. Romans 12:1, 2 . . . .

. . . .

. . . .

D. The choice is not once for all. Luke 9:23 . . . .

. . . .

. . . .

4. There are hindrances to Christ's Lordship. Read the verses and list each one next to the hindrance it refers to.

Mal. 3:8 _____ Priorities
Rom. 4:4-5 _____ Things (clothes, cars, etc.)
Luke 6:46 _____ Desire to be served
Luke 14:26 _____ Evil companions
John 5:44 _____ Pride of ability
Heb. 12:15 _____ Family
II Tim. 1:7 _____ Escapism (alcohol, drugs)
Matt. 6:33 _____ Seeking man's approval
Matt. 20:26 _____ Disobedience
Eccl. 5:10,11 _____ Pleasure
James 3:2 _____ Money
Prov. 23:7a _____ Sex
Prov. 14:30 _____ Lack of trust
Matt. 7:1 _____ Self-effort
Rom. 12:3 _____ Robbing God
Luke 12:15 _____ Fear
Mark 4:19 _____ Thought life
Rom. 8:28 _____ Critical Spirit
Rom. 13:12 _____ Bitterness
I Cor. 15:33 Ampl _____ Tongue
Eph. 4:26,27 _____ Resisting authority
Prov. 23:29-35 _____ Envy
    (Living)
I Cor. 6:18-20; _____ Anger
    Matt. 5:27, 28

5. From this list which two hindrances do you feel are the greatest today? ....
....
Circle the one you feel is your biggest problem at this time.

6. What will you do during this next week to allow God to deal with this area? How will you measure the results? (make it practical, personal and possible).

....
....
....
....
....

Tape BSU 95 — "Lordship of Christ"
Tape 2165 — "Jesus Is Lord"
Tape 1206 — "The Lordship of Christ"
Tape 684 — "The Lordship of Christ"
True Discipleship, by William MacDonald, Walterick publishers

CHAPTER VI

THE IMPORTANCE OF GOD'S WORD
[THE HAND]
(Used by permission of The Navigators)

The "Word Hand" shows us the five methods of learning from the Bible. Each of these methods is important.

Hearing the Word from godly pastors and teachers provides us insight into others' study of the Scriptures as well as stimulating our own appetites for the Word.

Reading the Bible gives us an overall picture of God's Word. Many find helpful a daily reading program which takes them systematically through the Bible.

Studying the Scriptures leads us into personal discoveries of God's truths. Writing down these discoveries helps us organize and remember them better.

Memorizing God's Word enables us to use the sword of the Spirit to overcome satan and temptations . . . to have it readily available for witnessing or helping others with a "word in season."

Meditation is the thumb of the Word Hand, for it is used in conjunction with each of the other four methods. Only as we meditate on God's Word — thinking of its meaning and application to our lives — will we discover its transforming power at work in us.

There are five basic ways we take in the Word of God. Since God is more interested in making us something than in simply teaching us something, (Eph. 1:12) how much of His Word we retain and apply is vitally important.

1. Match up the percentage of retention you feel would apply to each method of taking in the Word of God:

Hear	1	( ) 100%
Read	2	( ) 25-60%
Study	3	( ) 10-15%
Memorize	4	( ) 15-25%
Meditate	5	( ) 60-80%

2. Write out the following verses in your own words and place the references on the proper portion of the hand illustration.

A. Acts 17:11 ....

....

....

....

B. Romans 10:17 ....

....

....

C. Deut. 17:19 ....

....

....

D. Psalm 1:2, 3 ....

....

....

....

E. II Tim. 2:15 ....

....

....

....

F. Prov. 7:1-3 . . . .
. . . .
. . . .

G. Jer. 22:29 . . . .
. . . .
. . . .

H. I Tim. 4:15 . . . .
. . . .

I. Rev. 1:3 . . . .
. . . .

J. Psalm 119:9, 11 . . . .
. . . .
. . . .
. . . .

3. How many of these five ways do you feel are vital for a growing Christian? . . . .
. . . .
. . . .

4. Just a word about each of the ways:
   A. Hearing — don't neglect the fellowship of believers. Hebrews 10:25.
   B. Reading — If you have never read through the Bible completely in a year, why not start now? Four chapters a day will more than put you through. From year to year, why not use different translations? They will help keep your reading fresh and allow God to reveal to you different facets of His truth.
   C. Studying — study differs from reading in several ways. To study, the following elements should be present:
      1. Original investigation.
      2. Written reproduction.
      3. Consistency.
      4. Personal Application (See page 37)
      5. "Pass-on-able" (it should be so real to our lives that we can pass it on to others.)
   We will be experiencing several types of Bible study farther on in this booklet.

D. Memorizing — scripture memory pays dividends. It is not easy. It reaches the sub-conscious levels of our very being. Pray before attempting it. You will need God's help. Memory courses are available from:

The Navigators, Box 1659, Colorado Springs, Colorado

Moody Press, 820 N. LaSalle St., Chicago, Illinois

Bible Memory Association
P.O. Box 12,000
St. Louis, Missouri 63112

E. Meditation — this is spiritual digestion. It is getting the Word of God from the head to the heart and into the life.
Why not pray over the verses you are memorizing phrase by phrase as a form of meditation, or why not personalize the scripture as it is below for your meditation time:

Col. 3:10-16

"I am living a brand new kind of life that is continually learning more and more what is right, and trying constantly to be more and more like Christ who created this new life within me. In this new life, one's nationality or race or education or social position is not important; such things mean nothing — whether a person has Christ is what matters, and He is equally available to all. Since I have been chosen by God, who has given me this new kind of life, and because of His deep love and concern for me, I should practice tender hearted mercy and kindness to others. I should not worry about making a good impression on them, but be ready to suffer quietly and patiently. I should be gentle and ready to forgive, never holding grudges, and remembering that the Lord forgave me, so I must forgive others. I should let love guide my life, for then the whole church will stay together in perfect harmony. I will let the peace of heart which comes from Christ be always present in my heart and life, for this is my responsibility and privilege as a member of His Body, and I should always be thankful. I want to remember what Christ has taught and let His words enrich my life and make me wise. I would like to teach them to others and to sing them out in psalms and hymns and spiritual songs, singing to the Lord from a thankful heart."

5. Which way of scripture intake do you feel is most needed in your life currently? . . . .

6. What will you do in the next seven days to start correcting this lack? (every journey is made by taking the first step — make a start). . . . .
. . . .
. . . .
. . . .
. . . .

Suggestions For Further Study

Tape 1595 — "Intake of the Word"
Tape 1955 — "Scripture Memory"
Tape 820 — "Scripture Memory"
Tape 258 — "Bible Study"
Primer on Meditation, by The Navigators, Colorado Springs, Colorado

HOW TO MAKE A PERSONAL
APPLICATION FROM BIBLE STUDY

A. **What impresses me most?**
(Generally, as you study a subject or a portion, God by His Spirit will lay some particular aspect on your heart. Pray that God will open your eyes to a specific application. Ask Him what He wants you to do about it.)

B. **Where do I fall short in this?**
(When God speaks to you about a particular aspect of this study, write out the place where you fall short in this area. Use personal singular pronouns, I, Me, etc. An application should be *personal, practical and possible.* It should be concerned with a truth which may be translated into daily life and should be clearly stated. The application may deal with your relation to God or your relation to man. It should result in personal spiritual enrichment and uplifting by deepening your relationship to the Lord, or should improve your relationship to fellow Christians or those outside Christ.)

C. **What do I intend to do about it, with God's help?**
(Write out your intention as a definite action that you will take now to correct the weakness, build the needed quality into your life, strengthen the understanding, etc. This action may be memorizing a verse on the subject, or making a special study on it, or praying daily about the need. It may be writing a letter of apology, righting some harm done, etc. Whatever the action — *be specific.*)

THE GODLY WOMAN AS CHRIST'S REPRESENTATIVE

CHAPTER VII

BIBLICAL EXAMPLE — THE SHUNAMMITE WOMAN

This lesson is a type of character study. This is a very interesting and rewarding way of studying Biblical personalities. To encourage and aid you in doing other such studies on your own from the Bible, a sample outline you might wish to follow is included here:

Character Study Outline

1. List all the characteristics (good and bad) of the person to be studied.
2. Check a concordance to get verses of Scripture on these characteristics. (For instance: if the person was obedient to God, find a verse that speaks of the blessings of obedience, or the consequences of disobedience; if the person lied or hurt others by the use of his tongue, find a verse that tells what God thinks of wrong use of the tongue; if the person believed God for great things, find a verse that tells the value God places on such belief, or the consequences of unbelief, etc.) These are called "cross references" or "parallel passages."
3. Write a thumb-nail sketch or a brief summary of the person's life.
4. Write out problems. These can be things you don't understand about the person, or things you don't understand about God's dealings with him. State in the form of questions.
5. State what you think is the leading lesson taught by this life.
6. Make a personal application. (See page 37 for explanation.)

I. Study II Kings 4:8-37

. . . .
. . . .
. . . .
. . . .
. . . .

II. List all the characteristics and attitudes you see in her life—both good and bad.

. . . .
. . . .
. . . .
. . . .
. . . .
. . . .
. . . .
. . . .

III. List at least five of the above characteristics. From your own knowledge of the Bible, or using a concordance, find a cross-reference for each one. (See explanation on page 40, Number 2)

Characteristic   Cross-Reference

. . . .
. . . .
. . . .
. . . .
. . . .
. . . .
. . . .

IV. Write a brief summary of her life.

. . . .
. . . .
. . . .
. . . .
. . . .
. . . .
. . . .
. . . .
. . . .
. . . .
. . . .

V. What problems do you find in understanding either God's dealing with the Shunammite woman or her response to God or other people?

. . . .
. . . .
. . . .

. . .   .

VI. What do you think were some of this woman's attitudes
   A. Toward God? . . . .

   . . . .

   B. Toward her husband? . . . .

   . . . .

   C. Toward her child? . . . .

   . . . .

VII. What would you say is the leading lesson taught by her
   life?

   . . . .

   . . . .

   . . . .

   . . . .

VIII. What key insight about God did you discover while
   studying the life of the woman of Shunam?

   . . . .

   . . . .

   . . . .

   . . . .

IX. What trait do you see in the Shunammite woman that
   you would like to see in your own life?

   . . . .

X. Using the outline on page 37, write out what action you
   will take this week to make a personal application from
   this study.
   A. What impresses me most? . . . .

   . . . .

   B. Where do I fall short in this? . . . .

   . . . .

   C. What do I intend to do about it, with God's help?

   . . . .

   . . . .

   . . . .

   . . . .

CHAPTER VIII

CHARACTER & GUIDANCE SYSTEM OF A DISCIPLE
[THE BICYCLE]

In Psalm 78:71, 72, we read of God's calling David to be His people's shepherd (king). The testimony is that David cared for them in integrity of heart and with skillful hands. In the illustration of the Bicycle, "skillful hands" represents the back wheel. "Integrity of heart" represents the front wheel which is the character and guidance system of a disciple. It is possible to live the first year of the Christian life 20 times, instead of living 20 years of the Christian life. To insure that this does not happen, a person needs not only skill, but goals and guidance.

Before answering the questions, firmly fix these definitions in your mind:
—*Positive Mental Attitude:* Not negative; positive disposition and outlook.
—*Persistence:* Endurance; perseverance; not quitting or being sidetracked.
—*Drive:* Taking positive action, as an act of the will; not pampering the flesh and letting emotions or feelings control you; being highly motivated.
—*Mature Personality:* Full-grown; completely developed in one's individuality and disposition.

3. Write the key thought you see in each of the following Scriptures.

Phil. 4:8 ....

Joshua 14:10-12 ....

Heb. 10:36 ....

I Cor. 16:13 ....

Eph. 4:13 ....

Col. 1:18 ....

II Cor. 10:5 ....

Ps. 18:29 ....

Rev. 2:10 ....

II Cor. 4:16 ....

Gal. 4:19 ....

II Cor. 3:18 ....

Phil. 1:21 ....

Place the above Scripture references under the proper heading below.

POSITIVE MENTAL ATTITUDE

DRIVE

PERSISTENCE

MATURE PERSONALITY

—44—

4. Many factors combine to determine the character and guidance system of a disciple. Read the Scripture then place each of the traits of character in one of the four categories listed below:

Reliance on
  Christ II   Cor. 3:5
Faith in Christ   Phil. 4:13
Trust in Christ   Job 23:10
Dependance on
  Christ   Rom. 8:28
Expectancy   Phil. 4:19
Cheerfulness   Prov. 15:15
Enthusiasm   Josh. 6:20
Initiative   I Sam. 14:6
Decisiveness   James 1:8
          I Kings 18:2
Faithfulness   Luke 16:10
          Prov. 25:19

Patience   Heb. 6:15
Steadfastness   Eph. 6:13
Courage   Dan. 3:16-18
Self Control   I Cor. 9:26, 27
Servant Heart   I Cor. 9:19
Submissiveness to
  Authority   I Peter 5:5, 6
Teachableness   Prov. 10:8
Peacemaker   Psalm 133:1
Acceptance of
  Others   I Cor. 4:5
Humility   Phil. 2:3-4

POSITIVE MENTAL
ATTITUDE

....
....
....
....
....
....
....
....

DRIVE

....
....
....
....
....
....
....
....

PERSISTENCE

....
....
....
....
....
....
....
....

MATURE
PERSONALITY

....
....
....
....
....
....
....
....

5. While it is true that God has made each of us different and unique in personality, it is equally true that there are certain qualities we all need. Which two of the four categories would you most like to see strengthened in your own life? ....

. . . .

Why these two? . . . .

. . . .

. . . .

. . . .

. . . .

The Christian life is like riding a bicycle in many respects. If you don't move on, you will fall off. There are three main areas which cause people to falter in their Christian walk. They are the psychological, physical and the spiritual. A number of problems are caused because Christians lack a basic understanding of the emotional facts of what it means to walk with God.

PSYCHOLOGICAL: (Mental or Emotional)

Walking with God does not mean that we will always have perfect peace. II Cor. 6:10. Further, psychological conflict is not abnormal or sinful, but failure to resolve the conflict may be.

6. Match the scripture references with the psychological problems which can cause people to "fall off" in the Christian life.

You're bound to hear a discouraging word sometimes.

( ) Wrong mind set   1. I Cor.13:1-3
( ) Fear   2. I Jn. 2:15, 16
( ) Production oriented   3. II Tim. 1:7
( ) Worldliness   4. Heb. 12:1, 2A
( ) Guilt   5. Romans 13:1, 2
( ) Disappointment with God   6. John 5:44
( ) Disappointment with others   7. Heb. 12:15
( ) Disappointment with self   8. Psalm 12:1, 2LB
( ) Playing to wrong audience   9. Romans 7:15
( ) Bitterness   10. Psalm 38:4
( ) Rebellion against authority   11. Romans 9:20

7. Select two from the above list and explain in your own words how you would deal with them in your life or the life of another: ....
....
....
....
....
....
....
....
....
....
....
....

PHYSICAL:

8. An ineffective Christian walk may sometimes be traced to a physical root. List some of these causes below and their solutions:

CAUSE	SOLUTIONS
Psa. 102:3-5	Prov. 18:14; Psa. 4:1, 3-5 ..
....	....
Psa. 127:2	I Cor. 6:19, 20 ....
....	....
Prov. 13:4	Prov. 6:6-8 ....
....	....
Prov. 6:9-11	Prov. 10:4, 5; 20:13 ....
....	....
	....
	....

SPIRITUAL:

9. The psychological, physical, and spiritual lives are interdependent in most people. A few spiritual warnings are to be found in the following verses: Name them.

I Cor. 15:33 ....

Prov. 21:5 ....

James 3:5-10 ....

I Cor. 10:12 ....

John 15:5 ....

I Peter 2:1, 2 ....

I Cor. 4:7 ....

I Peter 5:8 ....

I Peter 5:5, 6 ....

10. The following remedies may be helpful in encouraging you to maintain balance and momentum in your Christian life:
   A. Make a genuine and total commitment of your life to God.
   B. Apply the necessary disciplines to walk with God in His Word, prayer and keeping short accounts with Him (keeping known sins confessed).
   C. Faith in the following:
      1. The sovereignty of God (He is in control) Ps. 115:3.
      2. The power of God (He can do anything) Jer. 32:17.
      3. The knowledge of God (He knows what is going on) Heb. 4:13.
      4. He is personally interested in you. John 10:3, 4; Luke 12:7.
   D. Maintain the vessel. I Cor. 9:26, 27. (A person in good physical and psychological condition will be in better shape spiritually).
   E. Be submissive to God rather than rebellious. James 4: 6, 7.
   F. Determine daily to be obedient to Him. I Sam. 15:22, 23; I Peter 3:10, 11.
   G. Determine to put to use any truth you learn (walk in the light) I John 1:7.
   H. Determine to profit from discipline or testing. Heb. 5:8, Heb. 12:6, Rev. 3:19.
   I. Have a goal of becoming spiritually educated through Bible study. Col. 1:9, 10, Col. 2:2, 3.
   J. Permit yourself to be exhorted or rebuked by other Christians when needed. Gal. 6:1, I Tim. 5:20, Heb. 10:25.
   K. Acquire the habit of intelligent and bold prayer. Eph. 6:18.
   L. Fight the good fight of faith. Prov. 3:5, I Peter 4:19, I Peter 5:7.

11. Review the 12 suggestions and list the two you feel are most needed in your life at this time. ....

....
....
....
....
....
....

12. How, spiritually, do you fail in these two areas? ....

....
....
....
....
....

A. What will you do about them this coming week? ....

....
....
....
....
....

B. How will you check up on yourself? ....

....

Suggestions for Further Study
Tape — BSU 155A — "Characteristics of a Disciple"
Spirit-Controlled Temperament and **Transformed Temperaments,** by Dr. Tim LaHaye, Tyndale House

CHAPTER IX

PRIORITIES, GOALS AND THE USE OF TIME

Today it seems that very few people feel they have enough time. There are some basic facts we need to know:

1. We all have the same amount of time.
2. We have all the time we need.
3. When we are pressured by time, it means either:
   A. We are doing the wrong things.
   B. We are doing the right things in the wrong way.

I. What do you learn about time and its use from Psalm 90:9 thru 12? ....

....

....

....

....

....

II. Define time: ....

....

....

....

III. Hebrews 1:2 (Amplified), "(But) in the last of these days He has spoken to us in (the person of a) Son, Whom He appointed Heir and lawful Owner of all things, also by and **through Whom He created** the worlds and the reaches of space and the **ages of time** — (that is), He made, produced, built, operated and arranged them in order."
Where did time come from? ....

IV. Whose time is it anyway? I Cor. 6:19, 20
CHECK ONE: Christ's ( ) Ours ( ) Everybody's ( )

V. According to I Cor. 4:2, we are .... of our time also. Explain what stewardship of time means. ....

....

....

....

VI. What do the following verses teach us regarding time from our point of view?

Psalm 39:4,   James 4:14   Psalm 90:9

. . . .
. . . .
. . . .
. . . .
. . . .
. . . .
. . . .
. . . .
. . . .

VII. Psalm 90:10 says our normal life span should be 70 years. How many days do you now have left? . . . .

What percentage of your life is already passed? . . . .

. . . .

In your imagination, project your life to its end. Now look back and decide what you would have wanted your life to have meant? This will assist you in setting priorities and goals.

VIII. Below are listed some areas of priorities with two scriptures for each of them. First match the scriptures with the areas. Then number the areas in the order of their importance as you think God sees them.

PRIORITY	AREAS		
( )	Husband	( )	( )
( )	Home	( )	( )
( )	Personal walk with Christ	( )	( )
( )	Ministry & Outreach	( )	( )
( )	Recreation	( )	( )
( )	Children	( )	( )
( )	Public relations (what others think)	( )	( )

3. Matt. 22:37, 38
4. Titus 2:4, 5
5. I Cor. 1:9
6. Col. 3:23
7. II Thess. 3:11, 12
8. Deut. 6:6, 7
9. II Cor. 5:19, 20
10. Mark 6:31
11. Prov. 31:11, 12
12. Matt. 28:18-20
13. Prov. 29:25
14. Gal. 1:10

VERSES
1. Prov. 22:6
2. Prov. 31:27

IX. If you feel your life style is not agreeing with priorities as God views them, what will you do specifically in one area this week to help re-align your life style to fit God's priorities? . . . .

. . . .

. . . .

. . . .

. . . .

STRONG PEOPLE HAVE GOALS, WEAK PEOPLE ONLY HAVE WISHES.

X. Search the following verses and select a basic pre-requisite for goal setting from each one. Write out the principle as you discover it from each verse.

Prov. 16:9 (Living) "We should make plans — counting on God to direct us." PRINCIPLE DISCOVERED . . . .

. . . .

. . . .

. . . .

. . . .

Prov. 23:23 (Living) "Get the facts at any price, and hold on tightly to all the good sense you can get." PRINCIPLE DISCOVERED: . . . .

. . . .

Acts 6:10 (Williams) "But they could not cope with his good practical sense and the spiritual power with which he usually spoke." PRINCIPLE DISCOVERED: . . . .

. . . .

. . . .

XI. Place the following verses (written out below) under their proper headings in goal preparation.

Verses:

I Kings 3:23 (Living) "Then the king said, 'let's get the facts straight: both of you claim the living child, and each says that the dead child belongs to the other.''

Prov. 22:3 (Living), "A prudent man foresees the difficulties ahead and **prepares** for them; the simpleton goes blindly on and **suffers** consequences."

Prov. 11:14 (New English Bible) "For want of skillful strategy an army is lost. Victory is the fruit of long planning."

I Kings 18:21 (Living), "Then Elijah talked to them. 'How long are you going to waver between two opinions?' he asked the people. If the Lord is God, follow him! But if Baal is God, then follow him!'"

HEADINGS	VERSES
Plan ahead	....
Get the facts	....
Use your head	....
Make a decision	....

1. Plan your time — if you don't, others will.
2. Leave a margin — for the unexpected.
3. Do one thing at a time and finish it.
4. Learn to say "NO." Giving an unqualified no answer is a mark of Christian maturity.
5. Separate the important from the urgent.
6. Use short cuts and helps which promote efficiency.
7. Be decisive. Do not be paralyzed by indecision.
8. Write it down. The poorest pencil has a better memory than the sharpest mind.
9. Be time conscious.

ASSIGNMENT:
Write out some of your current goals in the following areas and be prepared to share them:

1. Personal (spiritual, mental, emotional, physical, and social) ....
   ....
   ....
   ....
   ....

2. Family (husband, children and parents) ....
   ....
   ....
   ....
   ....
   ....

3. Home (schedule, projects, etc.) ....
....
....
....
....
....
....

4. Ministry (church, outreach, Bible study) ....
....
....
....
....
....
....

5. Recreational (sports, vacations, etc.) ....
....
....
....
....
....
....

6. Public Relations (community involvement, school participation, etc.) ....
....
....
....
....
....
....
....

Suggestions For Further Study
Tape 1273 AB — "Priorites and the Use of Time"
Tyranny of the Urgent — Intervarsity Press

CHAPTER X

FINDING GOD'S WILL

God is more interested in our knowing and doing His will than we are in discovering it. He is not trying to hide His will from us. His will is never in opposition to His Word.

I. God's revealed will is:
1. I Tim. 2:4 ....
   ....
2. I Thess. 4:3 ....
   ....
3. Gal. 1:4 ....
   ....
4. I Thess. 5:18 ....
   ....
5. I Peter 2:15 ....
6. I Peter 4:19 ....
7. Romans 14:9 ....

II. Principles in determining right or wrong.
   Christianity is not a set of rules but the operation of Divine principles. Some things are crystal clear as to their right-

ness or wrongness as revealed in the Bible. Other areas are not as clear. These areas need careful examination and decision by each of us.

Mark the following statements true or false in light of the Scriptures given.

1. If the Bible doesn't specifically condemn it, it is all right for me to do. I Cor. 6:12   T...F...
2. If the Bible speaks against it, I must not do it. Acts 5:29   T...F...
3. If it is socially acceptable, it is all right. Gal. 1:10   T...F...
4. If it could hurt my body, I must not do it. I Cor. 6:19, 20   T...F...

5. How it affects others is not really
important. Romans 14:21, II Cor.
6:3, I Cor. 11:1, I Cor. 10:33   T...F...

6. I should be concerned with whether it
glorifies God or not. I Cor. 10:31   T...F...

7. I am responsible for how it affects
my mind. Phil. 2:5   T...F...

8. If it is my time, life or money, I am
investing, then it is my own business. I Cor. 4:2   T...F...

III. Discovering God's will.

1. In Gensis 24:27, Abraham's servant was led by God because he was: (underline the correct answer)

A. A godly man
B. Wise
C. Moving in the direction of discovering God's will
D. Jewish

2. Psalm 119:105 teaches that clear leading for a life comes
from ....
....

3. Another way God leads us is through
Prov. 11:14.....................

4. Prov. 16:33 (Amplified) "The lot is cast into the lap, but
the decision is wholly of the Lord — even the events
(that seem accidental) are really ordered by Him,"
indicates that God can lead us through:
(underline one)
A. Throwing dice
B. Accidents
C. Circumstances

5. The inner conviction that a certain course of action is
right is called in Phil. 4:6, 7 ....

We have discovered that God leads us
through His Word, circumstances, inner peace and Godly counsel. He also
leads those who are moving instead of
sitting still. Remember, the most re-
liable leading is always the Bible.

IV. Procedures for discovering God's will. Study the following outline carefully and keep it handy as a reference for discovering God's will for your own life or helping another to determine what God would have him to do.

PROCEDURE FOR DISCOVERING GOD'S WILL

1. Do you believe that God's will can be known definitely and accurately? If not, look up Ps. 32:8 and Is. 30:21.
2. Are you willing to seek God's will and do it or would you just like to have an option on it? John 7:17
3. Have you made a permanent decision of commitment to be yielded to God for the rest of your life? If not, meditate on Rom. 12:1, 2 and seek counsel.
4. Is there any known unconfessed sin in your life? If so, stop here and confess it and forsake it. If you won't do that, then do not proceed in seeking God's will. I John 1:9, Prov. 28:13, Ps. 66:18
5. Are you obeying the known will of God for your life on a daily basis? If not, start today and demonstrate it before proceeding. Ps. 119.60, 00
6. Are you in neutral, willing for the matter to fall either way? Ask God to reveal whether you are in neutral. If not, continue to pray that God's desires will be your desires. Phil. 2:13
7. Are you praying specifically and definitely about it in faith? Make a list of your specific thoughts and pray about them. Pray in faith. James 1:5-7 (Living) Mark 10:51
8. Are you fellowshipping with God daily through reading His Word and prayer? If not, commit yourself to begin today. Ps. 5:3
9. Has God spoken to you through His Word, in your regular reading, or your scripture review? Keep a written record of what God speaks to you about. If you have been in the Word and have no guidance from it, continue in the Word but wait. Ps. 37:34 (Living)
10. Do you have *all* the available facts? If not, take action to get the facts. Prov. 24:3, 4 (Living)

11. Make a list here of advantages and disadvantages about the issue:

ADVANTAGES

. . . .
. . . .
. . . .
. . . .
. . . .
. . . .

DISADVANTAGES

. . . .
. . . .
. . . .
. . . .
. . . .
. . . .

12. What does common sense tell you to do? Acts 6:10 (Williams)
13. What do you want to do? Ps. 37:4
14. Why do you want to do it? Prov. 21:2 (Living)
15. Is it of benefit to you (spiritually, physically, emotionally, mentally, socially)? I Cor. 6:12
16. Will it be a thorn causing anxious cares, desire for riches, or desire for pleasure? Mark 4:19, Luke 8:14
17. Will it be a weight? Heb. 12:1, 2
18. Will it cause another to stumble? I Cor. 10:23, Rom. 14:21. Will it glorify God? I Cor. 10:31
19. Have you asked counsel from three spiritually mature people? If so, record what they said. If not, write the names of three you can ask:
    1. . . . .
    2. . . . .
    3. . . . .
    Prov. 15:22
20. Does it violate any known scriptural principle? Ps. 119:19 (Living)
21. Are you willing to wait in faith for God to line up His Word, your peace, and circumstances? Heb. 10:36
22. Do you have inner conviction or peace about a course of action? If so, proceed with conviction. Rom. 14:23

23. Act in faith, believing God wants you to do it. Heb. 11:6

V. Application: Review the principles in determing right or wrong. In the light of these principles, what are you now doing which you should stop or what are you considering doing which you should reject? What will you do about it?

. . . .

. . . .

. . . .

. . . .

. . . .

. . . .

Suggestions For Further Study
Tape 258A — "Will of God"
Tape 1533 — "Will of God"
Affirming the Will of God by Paul E. Little — Intervarsity Press
How to Know God's Will by Marion H. Nelson — Moody Press

CHAPTER XI

FINANCIAL RESPONSIBILITY

Money represents life because we must invest our lives to acquire it. Money is neither good nor bad, but becomes so only in the context of its use. It is a medium of exchange. Since it represents life, we are responsible for its use and handling. I Cor. 4:2, "Moreover it is required in stewards, that a man be found faithful."

I. Financial truths.
  1. Who really owns the world's riches? Haggai 2:8 . . . .
    . . . .
  2. Who gives us our ability to make money? Deut. 8:18, I Cor. 4:7 . . . .
  3. Match up some of the pitfalls of money with their appropriate scriptures:

( ) Forgetting God . . . . 1. Prov. 30:8, 9
( ) Stop trusting God . . . . 2. I Tim. 6:10
( ) Being deceived . . . . 3. Mark 4:19
( ) Falling in love with money . . . . . . 4. Deut. 8:12-14
( ) Trusting a fleeting commodity . . . 5. Prov. 23:4, 5
( ) Becoming ungrateful . . . . 6. Matt. 6:24
( ) Becoming double minded . . . . 7. Mal. 3:8
( ) Robbing God . . . . 8. Prov. 11:28 (Living)

"Trust in your money and down you go!
Trust in God and flourish as a tree."

  4. Do you feel prosperity or poverty is more spiritually helpful? . . . .
    Why? . . . .
    . . . .
  5. List a principle in finances from the following scriptures: Prov. 20:4, Prov. 14:23, II Thess. 3:10
    The principle is: . . . .
    . . . .

6. Prov. 21:20 (Living) says, "The wise man saves for the future, but the foolish man spends whatever he gets." What principle do we find in this verse regarding finances? . . . .

. . . .

7. Prov. 16:9 (Living) says, "We should make plans — counting on God to direct us." How does this apply in finances? . . . .

. . . .

. . . .

8. Prov. 17:18 (Living) says, "It is poor judgment to countersign another's note, to become responsible for his debts." What does this warn us against? . . . .

. . . .

9. What is our condition when we owe money? Prov. 22:7 .

. . . .

. . . .

10. Many people stay in debt because of a continuing practice of buying items which depreciate rapidly. Watch out for this trap. Romans 13:8 says we are to owe others only . . . .

. . . .

. . . .

11. God, in Phil. 4:19, has promised to provide our . . . .

. . . .

12. What is the difference between wants and needs? . . . . . .

. . . .

13. In Matthew 4:6, 7, the devil tempted Jesus to the sin of presumption. How can this sin be committed in the financial realm? . . . .

. . . .

. . . .

. . . .

. . . .

14. If you are short of money, answering the following questions may reveal to you the reason why this is true:
   A. Do I really need it?
   B. Is God testing my faith?
   C. Did I mis-spend the money God has already given me?
   D. Have I violated the financial principles?
   Match the scriptures with the principles:
   ( )   Stinginess   1. Luke 12:15
   ( )   Hastiness   2. Prov. 11:24, 25
   ( )   Stubbornness   3. Prov. 28:19, 20
   ( )   Laziness   4. Prov. 21:5
   ( )   Gluttony   5. Prov. 20:13
   ( )   Get-Rich-Quick Schemes   6. Prov. 23:21
   ( )   Coveteousness   7. Prov. 13:18

II. Another important principle in finances is giving. We will search for truths regarding why, how, and where to give.
   1. In the light of Deut. 14:23b (Living), "the purpose of tithing is to teach you always to put God first in your lives." Why do you feel God instituted tithing? . . . .
   . . . .
   . . . .

God is not nearly as interested in raising money as He is in raising children.

   2. What has God promised to those who give faithfully? Malachi 3:10 . . . .
   3. What would be the opposite effect which could come upon those who do not give faithfully? Malachi 3:11 . . .
   . . . .
   . . . .
   4. List some principles of giving to be found in II Cor. 9:6 thru 15. . . . .
   . . . .
   . . . .
   . . . .
   5. List some principles of giving to be found in II Cor. 8:1 thru 15 . . . .
   . . . .
   . . . .
   . . . .

6. Where should we give?
   A. Gal. 6:6 . . . .
   B. Prov. 19:17 . . . .
   C. James 2:15, 16 . . . .
   D. I Cor. 9:11-14 . . . .

   . . . .

ASSIGNMENT:
In the light of this study, discuss your financial situation with your husband to see if some changes need to be made. If they do, and you are in agreement, put them into effect immediately.

Suggestions For Further Study

Tape 1267 AB — "Financial Responsibility"

How to Live on your Income, Readers Digest Association, Pleasantville, New York

Guide to Personal Finance by Sal Nuccio, Harper & Row Publishers

You Can Be Financially Free by George Fooshee, Revell

CHAPTER XII

THE CHURCH

1. Define the church in your own words . . . .
   . . . .
   . . . .
   . . . .

2. Who owns the church? Acts 20:28 . . . .
   . . . .

3. Who is the head of the church? Col. 1:18 . . . .
   . . . .

4. What is God's desire for the church? I Cor. 1:9, 10 and Eph. 5:26, 27 . . . .
   . . . .

5. What has God promised to give His people? Jeremiah 3:15 . . .
   . . . .
   . . . .

6. What are these spiritual leaders to do? Acts 20:28 . . . .
   . . . .
   . . . .
   . . . .

   I Peter 5:2 . . . .
   . . . .

7. What is to be a spiritual leader's attitude? . . . .
   Luke 22:26 . . . .
   Mark 10:45 . . . .
8. What was the man's problem in Psa. 142:4? . . . .
   . . . .
   . . . .

9. Who is caring for your soul? . . . .
   According to I Cor. 4:15, we have many teachers, but only one
   spiritual parent. Write the name of the one person you
   look to for spiritual leadership more than any other . . . .

   . . . .

10. What should your response to your spiritual leader be? . . . . . .
    Hebrews 13:17 . . . .
    I Thess. 5:12, 13 . . . .
11. What do we learn from I Cor. 12:4-18 about what part we are
    to play in the operation of the church? . . . .

    . . . .

    . . . .
12. What does Hebrews 10:25 mean to you in the context of your
    church? . . . .

    . . . .
13. If we are not in agreement with spiritual leadership, what
    must we watch out for? I Sam. 24:6, I Chron. 16:22 . . . .

    . . . .

    . . . .

    . . . .
14. Whose responsibility is it to choose who fills the positions
    of spiritual leadership? Psa. 75:6, 7 . . . .

    . . . .

    I Tim. 1:5 in the 20th Century New Testa-
    ment says, "The object of all instruction is to
    call forth that love which comes from a pure
    heart, a clear conscience, and a sincere faith"
    and indicates that any instruction we are
    giving or receiving in the Christian context
    should eventuate in love.

15. What must a servant of God guard against? II Tim. 2:24, 25

    . . . .

    . . . .

    . . . .

    . . . .

ASSIGNMENT:
Gal. 5:22, 23 lists the fruit of the spirit. Meditate over these verses
and ask God to show you how you have fallen short of them in
your church relationship. Will you allow Him to correct this by
expressing Himself through you in the situation this coming
week? How? . . . .

    . . . .

    . . . .

    . . . .

. . . .
. . . .
. . . .
. . . .
. . . .
. . . .
. . . .
. . . .
. . . .

Suggestions For Further Study

Tape 602 — "The Servant Church"
Tape 603 — "The Teaching Church"

CHAPTER XIII

HELPING OTHERS

 Follow-up is parental care for spiritual babes. It is spiritual pediatrics. It means accepting spiritual responsibility for those God brings to you for help.

1. The book of I Thessalonians is a great revelation and exposition of follow-up principles. Read the book carefully, inserting the proper scripture references opposite the stated follow-up principle:

The objective of follow-up ....

Personal example ....

Individual care ....

Heart involvement ....

Practical helps ....

Prayer ....

Sharing of the life ....

Godly teaching ....

2. Various means of follow-up are available to us today, which were available to the early church. List some of them from the following verses:

I Cor. 4:17 ....

I Jn. 2:1, 2 ....

Phil. 1:3, 4 ....

Acts 15:36 ....

3. Since God is not as interested in how many we are as how much we count, spiritual maturity is a crying need. The Bible gives us examples of deeper relationships than merely follow-up. In these relationships, the imparting of life and encouraging to maximum maturity was taking place. Name the people involved in this type of deeper training, from the following passages:

I Tim. 2:2 ....

Acts 20:4 ....

II Kings 2:6 ....

Exodus 24:13 ....

Mark 3:13-15 ....

4. There are certain basic needs which all believers have. These are areas where the enemy generally attacks. Match the scriptures with the needs and then number them in their order of importance as you see it.

PRIORITY   NEEDS

( )   Feeding . . . .
           . . . .

( )   Protection . . . .
           . . . .

( )   Fellowship . . . .

( )   Assurance of salvation . . . .

( )   Daily Devotional life . . . .

( )   Ability to share testimony . . . .

( )   Ability to share the gospel . . . .

( )   Bible study . . . .

( )   Scripture Memory . . . .

( )   Prayer life . . . .

( )   Growing faith . . . .

SCRIPTURES

Luke 11:1	I Peter 5 :8	II Tim. 2 :15
I Peter 2:2, 3	Ps. 5 :3	Job 22 :21, 22
I John 5:11, 12	Ps. 107 :2	Col. 2 :6, 7
Ecc. 4:9, 10		Rom. 1 :16

ASSIGNMENT:

Write the name of one or more people you feel God would have you help in their spiritual walk. Get in touch with them some way this week. What you have already learned in this study booklet gives you a great deal to share in the way of follow-up.

Suggestions For Further Study

Tape BSU 56B — "Indispensable Principles of Training"

Tape 1 — "Born to Reproduce"

New Testament Follow-Up by Wayland B. Moore, Eerdman Publishers

Encouraging New Christians by Michael Griffiths, Inter Varsity Press

Follow-Up by Dawson E. Trotman, The Navigators, Colorado Spring, Colorado

Disciples Are Made—Not Born, by Walter Henrichsen, Victor Press

THE GODLY WOMAN

AS A

WIFE

"The Lord said . . . I will make him a suitable helper, completing him." Gen. 2:18 (Berkeley)

INTRODUCTION TO FAMILY STUDIES

In the world of the Twentieth Century, with its uncertainty, its crumbling value systems and its many social problems and pressures, thinking people are concerned about the home. They are seeking guide lines for effective and fulfilling marriage relationships.

These studies are designed to help improve our understanding of Christian marriage with its challenges, joys, and satisfactions . . . and to produce a distinctively Christian home where Christ lives—not merely a home where Christians live.

The studies leave much unsaid, but this is inevitable within the limits of a single book.

We would highly recommend that you read *Heaven Help the Home* by Howard Hendricks, Victor Press and *How to Be Happy Though Married*, by Dr. Tim LaHaye, Tyndale House, as companion study books for these chapters on marriage, children and the home. These books are on the art and joy of successful family living and cover much of what's been left unsaid in these brief studies. Other helpful tapes and books are listed at the end of each chapter.

CHAPTER XIV

THE BASIS OF MARRIAGE

1. How did God create man? Genesis 1:26, 27

   . . . .
   . . . .
   . . . .

2. Why did God establish the marriage relationship? Genesis
   2:18 . . . .

3. Men and women desire to be married for various reasons. What are some of these motivations?

   MEN   WOMEN

   . . . .
   . . . .
   . . . .
   . . . .
   . . . .
   . . . .

4. In the Bible, God uses marriage to describe the relationship of Christ to the individual believer. What are some
   of the parallels you see between these two relationships?

   . . . .
   . . . .
   . . . .
   . . . .
   . . . .
   . . . .

5. God has given certain scriptural principles which provide
   the basis of a truly Godly marriage. From the following
   Scriptures, state as many of these principles as you can
   find. Genesis 2:18, 24; Eph. 5:21-33; Col. 3:18, 19; I Cor.
   7:3-5; I Cor. 11:3; Genesis 18:19; Genesis 1:26-28.

6. The following are some general principles God has given to Christians. State the principle and how it also contributes to a Godly marriage.

Ephesians 5:18

I Thess. 5:18

Eph. 4:26

Col. 3:23

Eph. 4:31, 32

I Pet. 4:9, Rom. 12:13

Col. 2:6, 7 (Living)

Phil. 4:6, 7

Phil. 2:3, 4

Rom. 13:8

II Cor. 6:14 ....
....

7. Which of these principles for a godly marriage is most
   lacking in your marriage? What can you do this week to
   begin to change this? ....
   ....
   ....
   ....

   In order to have a godly marriage, there must be godly
   partners. The basis of a godly marriage begins with the
   individual.

8. From the following Scriptures, what are some basic truths
   that must be evident for God to express His likeness in
   us? ....
   A. John 15:5 ....

   B. II Cor. 3:18 ....
   C. John 3:30 ....
   D. II Peter 1:4 ....
9. What characteristics relating to godliness do you see in
   these Scriptures?
   A. Genesis 6:9 ....
   B. Heb. 11:8 ....
   C. Num. 14:6-8 ....
   D. I Kings 4:29 ....
   E. Num. 32:12 ....

10. In Genesis 18:19 and Ephesians 5:22-24, we found that the husband is to lead the family. In what areas is he to lead?

....
....

Is this true in your family? ....
11. How can a husband who desires to lead his family be kept from it? ....
....
....
....

12. Briefly describe the influence of the men and women in the following verses.
I Peter 3:7 ....
Matt. 27:19-26 ....
I Sam. 25:14-35 ....
....
1 Kings 11:1-4 ....
....
I Kings 21:4-16 ....
....
II Kings 4:8-10 ....
....
Esther 4:14-16; 7:3-6; 8:4-8 ....
....

(This reveals how greatly men can influence women, and women can influence men—for good, or for evil.)
13. Who is answerable to God for setting the direction of the home?
A. I Tim. 3:4, 5 ....
B. I Cor. 11:3 ....
C. Col. 3:18-21 ....
14. List the responsibilities of the husband and the wife in the family and home as you understand them.

HUSBAND	WIFE
....	....
....	....
....	....
....	....
....	....

15. What if a husband or wife is not fulfilling his/her God-given role—What can the other partner do about it? (I John 3:21, 22; Matt. 21:22; Col. 3:23) . . . .

16. In which of these responsibilities do you feel least adequate? . . . .

What will you do this week to allow God to help you in this area?

Suggestions For Further Study

Tape 577 — "The Foundation of The Scriptural Home"
Tape 1059 — "Survey of our Need and God's Provision"
Tape 1057 — "Husband-Wife Relationship"

Building A Christian Home, by Brandt and Dowdy, Victor Books

The Christian Family, by Larry Christenson, Bethany Fellowship.

Ms. Means Myself, by Gladys Hunt, Zondervan.

Creative Counterpart by Linda Dillow, Nelson

Magnificent Marriage by Gordon McDonald, Tyndale

The Fulfilled Woman by Beardsley and Spry, Harvest House

You Can Be The Wife of a Happy Husband by Cooper, Victor Books

CHAPTER XV

THE GODLY WOMAN
BEING "A HELPER FIT FOR HIM"

PART I
(FOLLOW THE LEADER)

Marriage is a trinity — even as God is a trinity. The parts of marriage are: spiritual, emotional and physical. Like a three-legged milk stool — if one part is missing, it becomes ineffective in its operation. Further, the very nature of marriage in its intimacy reveals the weaknesses and shortcomings of each partner. With this knowledge comes the ability to hurt deeply. We are charged before God with the privilege and responsibility of completing our husbands, of being "a helper fit for him" (Genesis 2:18). Therefore, we desperately need to know and understand the needs of our husbands and to take the necessary steps to meet them. Only in this way can we adequately fulfill our responsibility and privilege.

A. *HIS PART AND MINE — Or, Where Do I Fit In?*
1. Study the following verses: Genesis 2:18; Eph. 5:22-33; Col. 3:18, 19; I Peter 3:7.
Using the information found in these verses, write a definition for:
a. The role of the husband . . . .
. . . .
. . . .
. . . .
. . . .
b. The role of the wife . . . .
. . . .
. . . .
. . . .
. . . .

God's role for a wife is to be a completer, not a competer.

2. The role of the wife is a supportive role. From the following verses list some of the ways a wife should support her husband.

Eph. 5:24 ....

Proverbs 31:12 ....

I Peter 3:6 (Living) ....

Eph. 5:33 (Living & Amplified) ....

....

....

I Peter 3:1 ....

....

Prov. 31:11 ....

I Thess. 5:17 ....

Col. 3:13 ....

....

Eph. 4:26, 27 ....

Eph. 4:2, 3 (Living) ....

....

....

3. According to Eph. 5:24, 25, what one word summarizes God's chief command to:

husbands? ....

wives? ....

4. Check several sources, then formulate a definition of *submission*.

....

....

....

....

5. From Eph. 5:22-24, what do we learn about submission? ....

....

....

....

"Many modern women do not like the idea of being subject to a man because they do not know the inner meaning of the command, 'Be subject.' Both the Greek and Latin words carry the idea of throwing oneself under, as a foundation, as an assistant, or to use the biblical phrase concerning our first parents, 'a helper fit for him' (Gen. 2:18, 20)."

—Donald Grey Barnhouse

6. Why do you think God requires the role of submission rather than the role of leadership for wives? . . . . . .

. . . .

7. Comment on this statement: "Submission is an attitude before it is an act."

. . . .

. . . .

8. Answer the following yes/no questions and then explain why you gave that answer to each question.
   A. Can a woman be truly submitted to God and not to her husband? . . . .
   Explain: . . . .

   . . . .

   B. Does the husband's headship mean he is to operate as a dictator? . . . .
   Explain: . . . .

   . . . .

   C. Does the headship of the husband and the submission of the wife indicate that man is superior and woman is inferior? . . . .
   Explain: . . . .

   . . . .

   D. Should a wife always submit to her husband, or only when she thinks he's right? . . . .
   Explain: . . . .

   . . . .

   E. Does the husband's headship mean he makes all the decisions? . . . .
   Explain: . . . .

   . . . .

   There is no position of superiority or inferiority when a husband and wife fulfill their God-appointed roles. Each has a different—but equally important role. They are like a lock and key— neither is more important than the other, and neither can fulfill its function without the other.

9. Is there an area of your life in which you are not submissive to your husband (and therefore not submissive to Christ)?
What will you do about it this week?

What other area of the supportive role (question #2) do you need to improve in?

What will you do this week to improve in that area?

"GOD REQUIRES SUBMISSION OF WOMEN BECAUSE IT SUITS THEIR NEEDS — NOT HIS."

—Howard Hendricks

B. *THE NEVER-FAIL FORMULA*
1. Without using reference material, write out your definition of love.

2. Read I Cor. 13 in several translations. Write out the one thing which stands out to you most.

3. From verses 1-3, list some things which are good in themselves, but which are worthless without love.

4. True love always expresses itself. The following
   action words for love have been taken from several
   translations of the Bible. Take each one and write
   out in your own words:
   a) what it means b) how it works in the home
   1. Love is patient.
       a) ....
          ....
       b) ....
          ....
   2. Love is kind.
       a) ....
          ....
       b) ....
          ....
   3. Love is not jealous.
       a) ....
          ....
       b) ....
          ....
   4. Love is not boastful.
       a) ....
          ....
       h) ....
          ....
   5. Love has good manners.
       a) ....
          ....
       b) ....
          ....
   6. Love is not selfish.
       a) ....
          ....
       b) ....
          ....
   7. Love rejoices in right.
       a) ....
          ....
       b) ....
          ....
   8. Love is not arrogant.
       a) ....

b) ....

9. Love is not irritable.
   a) ....

   b) ....

10. Love is not resentful.
    a) ....

    b) ....

5. From verse 7 of I Cor. 13, choose the one aspect which seems most important to you. Give an example of how it should work in marriage or in the home.
   1. My choice: ....

   2. How it should work: ....
   ....

6. From I Cor. 13:1-7:
   1. What is your greatest need at this time?
   ....
   ....

   2. How does this need manifest itself?
   ....
   ....

   3. What steps will you take this week, with God's help, to improve in this area of need?
   ....
   ....
   ....

Suggestions For Further Study

Tape 1060 — "Difficulties In The Walk of Love"
Tape 1061 — "Submission"
Tape 1155 — "Role and Responsibility of the Wife"
Tape 1180 — "Wife's Responsibility"
For Women Only, by Peterson, Tyndale House
Me, Obey Him? by Elizabeth Handford, Sword of the Lord

THE GODLY WOMAN
BEING "A HELPER FIT FOR HIM"

PART II

(HIS HOME IS HIS CASTLE)

A. *SETTING THE ATMOSPHERE OF THE HOME*
A wife is called upon to create the environment and right climate in which the tender plants of love and marriage can grow and flourish.
  1. Think back through the past week:
     a. In the time shared with your husband before he left the house, what kind of atmosphere did you set for the day?

     . . . .
     . . . .
     . . . .

     b. When you greeted him upon returning home, what kind of atmosphere did you set for the remainder of the day or evening?

     . . . .
     . . . .
     . . . .

  2. What principles for helping to set a good atmosphere in the home do you find in Eph. 4:26-27, 29-32?

     . . . .
     . . . .
     . . . .
     . . . .
     . . . .
     . . . .

  3. What do you think your own attitude and appearance have to do with setting the atmosphere? Explain.

     . . . .
     . . . .
     . . . .

4. What have you taught your children regarding how they can help set a good atmosphere when their daddy arrives home? . . . .

. . . .

. . . .

. . . .

B. *FULFILLING YOUR HUSBAND'S NEEDS*

1. Try to put yourself in your husband's place: What do you think he needs most during the first 30 minutes after arriving home from work? . . . . . .

. . . .

. . . .

2. How do you greet your husband when he comes home? (e.g.—with a "recital" of all the problems you've faced during the day? with a loving look, or word, or touch? with indifference? with coldness? with joy and warm affection? with "If you think you've had a hard day, wait until you hear about mine!"?) . . . .

. . . .

3. How can you apply Mark 10:45 in this matter of meeting your husband's needs? . . . .

. . . .

. . . .

. . . .

. . . .

4. What is your honest desire – to "minister" to your husband, or to "be ministered unto" by him?

. . . .

. . . .

5. How can you apply the promise given in Luke 6:38 to your situation?

. . . .

. . . .

. . . .

. . . .

. . . .

Some of a husband's greatest needs are: (a) to be admired; (b) to know he's important to you; (c) to have you show interest in him and in his work; (d) to be accepted just the way he is.

6. What are you doing to meet your husband's need for admiration? ....
....
....

7. List the things you admire about your husband's manliness. ....
....
....
(Now look for opportunities to *tell* him these things!)

8. How do you communicate to your husband that he is very important, very "special" to you? ....
....
....

9. What keeps you from showing your husband you are interested in him and his work? ....
....
....

10. TRUE/FALSE. Demonstrating to your husband that you accept him involves:
    a. Expressing your acceptance ....
    b. Maintaining a self-righteous attitude ....
    c. Using other men as a shining example ....
    d. Looking to his better side ....

11. On a separate sheet, list all of your husband's good-characteristics—all the things that first made you love him, things that make up his "better side."

12. During this week look for many natural opportunities to verbalize your appreciation of these good characteristics he possesses. Make a check mark by each one you are able to share with him. (Keep the list handy to add to, and to refer to when negative thoughts begin to crowd into your mind and dominate your thinking.)

C. *COMMUNICATION*

"The heart of marriage is its communication system. It can be said that the success and happiness of any married pair is measurable in terms of the deepening dialogue which characterizes their union."   **—Dwight Small**

1. Define Communication:

2. On a scale of 1-10 (with 10 being the highest or best), how would you rate the communication between you and your husband?

3. In your opinion, what are some causes that hinder, or block, or even cause meaningful communication to cease?

4. Words are not the only communicators. How else do we communicate?

Suppose a wife greets her husband with "I thought you'd never get home." The various messages a wife could be giving in this statement and how a husband would interpret the meaning of the words are:

5. What part does attentive listening play in good communications? . . . .

. . . .

. . . .

6. What does Amos 3:3 teach us about communications?

. . . .

. . . .

7. COMMUNICATION AIDS. Under each verse below list: 1) The basic principle described in this verse, 2) the opposite of this principle, and 3) the problems in communication caused by not following this principle.

   A. Eph. 4:15

      1) . . . .

         . . . .

      2) . . . .

         . . . .

      3) . . . .

         . . . .

   b. Eph. 4:26-27

      1) . . . .

         . . . .

      2) . . . .

         . . . .

      3) . . . .

         . . . .

   c. Eph. 4:29

      1) . . . .

         . . . .

      2) . . . .

         . . . .

      3) . . . .

         . . . .

d. Prov. 15:1
   1) ....
   ....
   2) ....
   ....
   3) ....
   ....

e. Prov. 18:13
   1) ....
   ....
   2) ....
   ....
   3) ....
   ....

f. James 1:19
   1) ....
   ....
   2) ....
   ....
   3) ....
   ....

8. In the following verses what are the problems or barriers to communication in a marriage.

PROBLEMS OR BARRIERS   SCRIPTURES

_____ Luke 6:31
_____ Prov. 13:10
_____ Eph. 4:31
_____ Eph. 4:26
_____ Phil. 2:3,4
_____ Prov. 10:8
_____ Esther 4:11
_____ John 3:19,20
_____ Is. 53:6
_____ Jeremiah 17:9

9. If a couple was having problems communicating and asked your help, what advice or counsel would you give them?

. . . .

. . . .

. . . .

. . . .

. . . .

10. Where do you fall short in communication?

. . . .

. . . .

What one thing will you do this week to improve the situation? . . . .

. . . .

. . . .

. . . .

Non-verbal communication can do a great deal to deepen love's dialogue. What things that are important to your husband will you do this week to communicate to him nonverbally "I love you"?

. . . .

. . . .

. . . .

D. *GODLY HOMEMAKING*

"Being a homemaker is the great adventure God entrusted to a married woman, and her influence spreads beyond her imagination. It will take the very best any woman has to offer. It cannot be her casual interest; it must be her major concern. It will drive her to a life with God that is deep and rich and will mean the unconscious expansion of her puny soul." —Gladys M. Hunt

1. Circle the word(s) that make this statement true: My husband does/does not enjoy our home. What explanation can you give for this? . . . .

. . . .

. . . .

. . . .

Phillips Brooks said, "Duty makes us do things well, but love makes us do them beautifully."

2. Use the following words as you write a paragraph on "Being a Godly Homemaker":

contentment, perfection, selfishness, consistency, sense of humor, prayer, schedule, consideration of needs and desires of family, creativity, outside activities, compulsiveness, comfort, beauty

BEING A GODLY HOMEMAKER

. . . .

. . . .

. . . .

. . . .

. . . .

. . . .

. . . .

. . . .

. . . .

. . . .

3. Ask your husband how you may improve and please him more in your role as homemaker. Thank him for his suggestions and begin to carry them out.

Suggestions For Further Study
Tape 1063 — "Atmosphere of the Home"
Tape 1062 — "Communication Between Husband and Wife"
Tape 2136 — "Communication an Art to be Learned"
Tape 2137 — "Simplifying Life"
Total Woman, by Marabel Morgan, Fleming Revell
Communication, Key to Your Marriage by Norman Wright, Regal

THE GODLY WOMAN
BEING "A HELPER FIT FOR HIM"
PART III

(BEING HIS QUEEN)

One definition Webster gives for the word "Queen" is: "A woman foremost, or judged to be foremost among others in certain attributes or accomplishments."

The goal of each wife should be "to be foremost among others in certain attributes or accomplishments" which are important to her husband so that he will exclaim:

"There are many fine women in the world, but you are the best of them all." Proverbs 31:29 (Living)

The queenly attributes or accomplishments which we will cover are: attitudes, appearance, and character.

A. *ATTITUDES*
1. Match up the following bad attitudes with one of the verses of Scripture.
   a. Nagging .... Prov. 17:9
   b. Self-pity, complaining ...... Prov. 12:25
   c. Being negative & critical .... Prov. 21:9 (Amp.)
   d. Being a dream-buster .... Jude 16 (Berkeley)
   e. Talking too much .... Num. 13:27-33
   f. Having bitterness, resentment .... Prov. 18:2
   g. Never letting a matter die (continuing to rehearse an offense or mistake) .... Heb. 12:15
2. Study Proverbs 14:1 and then write in your own words what this means to you. ....
....
....

3. The following verses offer some antidotes for bad attitudes: Matt. 21:22; Phil. 4:8; Isa. 43:18; I Thess. 5:18; Prov. 14:1; Eph. 4:31, 32; Psa. 141:3.

Find the positive antidote in each of the above verses and list it beside the bad attitude it would best help eliminate.

	Verse	Antidote
Nagging		
Self-pity, complaining		
Negative, critical		
Dream-buster		
Talking too much		
Bitterness or resentment		
Never letting a matter die		

4. Which of these negative attitudes are you most guilty of? . . . .

. . . .

What will you do this week to break this habit pattern and allow God to change you? . . . .

. . . .

. . . .

B. *APPEARANCE*
1. Is I Peter 3:3, 4 speaking of prohibition or priority?

. . . .

Explain your answer . . . .

. . . .

2. I Sam. 16:7—If God looks on the heart, why does our appearance matter? . . . .

. . . .

. . . .

3. Answer the following questions with a "yes" or "no".
   a. Do you consult your husband about your choice of clothes? . . . .
   b. Does he cast the deciding vote on the clothes you buy? . . . .
   c. Do you dress to please him? . . . .
   d. Do you wear things he disapproves of? . . . .
   e. Are you paying less attention to keeping attractive now than before your marriage? . . . .

f. Do you seek to freshen up and look attractive before your husband arrives home? . . . .

4. What should be the motive and guiding principles for the Christian wife in determining her appearance? See Matt. 5:16, Luke 16:10 . . . .
. . . .
. . . .

5. What will you work on this week to seek to be more attractive to your husband? . . . .
. . . .
. . . .
. . . .
. . . .

C. CHARACTER

Character is a person's distinctive qualities or traits.

1. Integrity
   a. Define integrity in your own words . . . .
   . . . .
   . . . .

   b. What truths about integrity can be discovered from the following verses?
      1) Job 2:3 . . . .
      . . . .
      2) Ps. 7:8 . . . .
      . . . .
      3) Ps. 25:21 . . . .
      . . . .
      4) Ps. 41:12 . . . .
      . . . .
      5) Prov. 11:3 . . . .
      . . . .
      6) Prov. 20:7 . . . .
      . . . .

2. Consistency and Faithfulness
   a. What do we learn about our God from Mal. 3:6 and Heb. 13:8? . . . .
   . . . .

   b. How does this apply to us in our marriage relationship? . . . .

c. What does James 1:8 warn against? ....

d. Why did his enemies have difficulty in finding fault with Daniel? Dan 6:4 ....

e. What kind of a servant did Jesus commend in Matt. 25:21? ....

f. What can we discover about faithfulness from Luke 16:10, 11 ....

3. Emotional Stability and Maturity
   a. How would you define emotional stability and maturity? ....

   b. List some characteristics that are evident in one who is emotionally stable and mature.

   c. What one thing out of this list are you most lacking in? .... What will you do this week with God's help to bring that area of weakness or sin under Christ's control? ....

   d. What negative emotions do you find most difficult to handle? (e.g. anger, envy, jealousy, nervousness, anxiety, etc.) ....

e. What helps you most to overcome times of depression or "feeling low"? . . . .
. . . .
. . . .
. . . .

Remember, our negative emotions and other negative personality traits CAN be changed to the degree that our lives are brought under the control of the Holy Spirit. He is in the business of transforming our temperaments as we learn to walk in the Spirit. Tim LaHaye has two very excellent books on this which we highly recommend: *Transformed Temperaments* and *Spirit-Controlled Temperament*.

Suggestions For Further Study
Tape 1062 — "Women's Moods"
Tape 1295 — "God's Beauty Course"
How To Win Over Depression, by Dr. Tim LaHaye, Zondervan

THE GODLY WOMAN
BEING "A HELPER FIT FOR HIM"
PART IV
(SEX IS FUN—ENJOY IT!)

The sexual part of marriage is perhaps the least spoken to, and yet one of the most important. The Bible gives some clear directions which we will do well to heed.

1. When did God create sex? Gen. 1:27, 28 . . . .
. . . .
Was this before or after sin entered the world?
. . . . Therefore, is the
sexual relationship within marriage sinful? . . . .
2. Why is sexual intercourse wrong outside of marriage and right within the bonds of marriage?

. . . .

. . . .

. . . .

Marriage and sex are of divine origin. Grace perfects them. Sin perverts them.
3. From the following verses, list some reasons you believe God instituted sex and marriage. . . . .
Ps. 127:3-5 . . . .
I Cor. 7:2-5 . . . .
Gen. 2:24 . . . .
4. Write out in your own words the meaning of I Cor. 7:2-5 and then write how this should operate in marriage.

. . . .

. . . .

. . . .

. . . .

. . . .

. . . .

. . . .

5. Explain what you think is meant by this statement:
"A woman's greatest sex organ is her mind."

. . . .

. . . .

. . . .

. . . .

The sex act to a man is mainly physical. To a woman it is not only physical but emotional and spiritual. It is the closest thing to totally giving herself that a woman can express in an act. This being true, a woman will not and cannot function well sexually while torn up emotionally. A satisfactory sexual relationship is mainly a husband's project. A sexual conflict may exist between husband and wife if there is a feeling of competition, resentment carried over from courtship, too large an age difference or differing sexual drives. The husband may have personal problems of feeling inadequate sexually, or being domineering and selfish. The wife's problem may spring from inner fears, pain in the relationship, puritanical ideas, or feelings of guilt and being used instead of loved. Sexual conflict may also be caused by a physical health problem in either party, a lack of time (too much to do) or simply tiredness. The first step in solving any problem is determining the cause.

6. How would you counsel a woman who came to you with the following problems:
   A. Intercourse is just a duty to me which I escape as often as possible. . . . .

   . . . .

   B. I feel it would be wrong for me to really enjoy sex.

   . . . .

   . . . .

   . . . .

   C. I withhold sex as a weapon to get my own way or as a punishment when my husband displeases me.

   . . . .

   . . . .

   . . . .

   D. I don't get any fulfillment or satisfaction or release from sexual intercourse. . . . .

. . . .

. . . .

E. My husband gets satisfied very quickly and often leaves me frustrated. . . . .

. . . .

. . . .

F. My husband seems to think only of sex! He wants sexual relations far more often than I do. . . . .

. . . .

. . . .

G. By the time we're ready for bed, I'm too tired to think of having intercourse. . . . .

. . . .

. . . .

H. My sexual desire and ability to be sexually aroused seems to be dwindling. What should I do?

. . . .

. . . .

. . . .

Remember, love gives. It is the nature of love to want to give. It looks for ways of expression. God planned that intercourse be the deepest expression of love and oneness we are capable of: Love is never selfish. It does not seek self-satisfaction first. Love sees sex as a desire for an interaction and communion of the total personality.

7. Using the Scriptures given in this chapter (and other Bible verses with which you are familiar) write a summary paragraph on what the Bible has to say about the sexual relationship between husband and wife. . . . .

. . . .

. . . .

. . . .

. . . .

. . . .

Some keys to a good sexual relationship with your husband are: prayer, right attitude, sweet-smelling cleanliness, unselfishness, patience.

ASSIGNMENT: Many sexual problems in marriage are caused by lack of communication on the part of one partner or the other as to personal likes and dislikes regarding the sex act. Pray for boldness to openly discuss this with your husband so that both of you may experience an ever-increasing joy in each other as God intends.

Suggestions For Further Study

Tape 1154 — "Marriage and God's Purpose For Sex"

Tape 1863 — "The Other Side of Sex"

Tape 2135 — "Sex Is God's Idea and It's Fun"

Sexual Happiness In Marriage, by H. J. Miles, Zondervan

How to be Happy Though Married, by Dr. Tim LaHaye, Tyndale House

Physical Unity in Marriage, by Shirley Rice, the Tabernacle Church, 7120 Granby, Norfolk, Va.

The Act of Marriage by Tim and Beverly LaHays, Zondervan

Intended for Pleasure by Wheat, Revell

(Two very excellent tapes on the sexual relationship in marriage are also available from the free lending library of Dr. Ed Wheat, Springdale, Arkansas.)

CHAPTER XVI

USING THE HOME AS
A PLACE OF MINISTRY

A Christian home is a mighty tool in the hands of God to convince a lost and dying world of the reality of Jesus Christ. The warm atmosphere of such a home is often the climate necessary to bring a skeptical unbeliever to the point of considering the claims of Christ. Having friends in for coffee or for a meal, starting a neighborhood Bible discussion group, making the home available for prayer groups, and allowing God to express Himself to others through hospitality, are some ways a home can be used.

1. Home is a place to which people come or from which people go.

   A. Which of these is more important? ....
   Why ....
   ....
   ....
   ....
   ....

   B. How would you define hospitality? Titus 1:8, Romans 12:13 ....
   ....

   C. What is the significance of giving a person a meal? See Luke 19:5-10, Luke 24:28-31 ....
   ....

2. In the story recorded in Luke 10:29-37, how would you describe a neighbor? ....
   ....

3. What was the governing power behind Paul's ministry? II Cor. 5:14, 15 ....

4. What is the purpose of ministering to others? Eph. 4: 11-16, Col. 1:28, 29 ....
   ....

5. Note the following examples of hospitality. Write down (a) who gave the hospitality   (b) who received it, and (c) what blessings the ones who gave the hospitality received as a result of it. (You may have to read further in the assigned portions to discern this.)

Gen. 18:1-8

A.

B.

C.

Gen. 24:17-20

A.

B.

C.

Joshua 2:1-16

A.

B.

C.

I Kings 17:10-24

A.

B.

C.

II Kings 4:8-11

A.

B.

C.

Luke 10:38-42

A.

B.

C.

Acts 16:14, 15

A.

B.

C.

6. To whom should we offer hospitality?

A. Leviticus 19:33, 34

B. Isaiah 58:7

C. Matt. 25:34-46

D. I Peter 4:9

E. III John 5-8 . . . .

7. What are some of the reasons we should show hospitality?
   A. Isaiah 60:11 . . . .
   B. Eccl. 11:1 . . . .
   C. Heb. 13:1, 2 . . . .
8. To whom are we not to extend hospitality? II John 10-11

. . . .
9. Who is the most hospitable couple you know? . . . .

. . . .
Write out the outstanding characteristics, as you see them,
which make them hospitable. . . . .

ASSIGNMENT
Real hospitality is costly in time, privacy, involvement, and
money. Do you think the investment is worth it? . . . .
If so, discuss with your partner how your home can be used to
minister to others more effectively. Write out a plan and
schedule as to how and when your home will become a more
available tool in the hands of God for the blessing of others.

Suggestions For Further Study
Tape 1021 — "Use of the Home in the Ministry"
Tape 1279 — "Hospitality"
Ms. Means Myself, (chap. 7), by Glady Hunt, Zondervan

THE GODLY WOMAN
AS A
MOTHER

CHAPTER XVII

RESPONSIBILITIES
TO OUR CHILDREN

"Your children are God's assignment or commission, and He does not waste children on parents. He knows the very kind to send you. Did you think God gave you children because of what you could do for them? That's only one part. He gave them because of what they could do for you. You can meet your children's particular needs and they can meet yours in a unique and special way."—Howard Hendricks

1. What are the various words used in Psalm 127 to describe children? ....

   ....

   ....

   What do each of these words mean to you? ....

   ....

   ....

   ....

2. Who is responsible for training the children?
   A. Proverbs 1:8 ....
   B. Proverbs 29:15-17

   ....
   What is the mother's responsibility? ....

   ....

3. What are the parents' responsibilities in the following verses:
   A. Eph. 6:4 ....
   B. Deut. 6:4-7 ....
   C. Prov. 2:1, 3:1, 4:1, 5:1, 7:1 ....

   ....

   ....

   ....

4. How are we to love our children?
   A. Matt. 3:17 ....
   B. Gen. 22:2 ....

C. II Sam. 18:33 ....

D. Luke 8:40-42 & 49-56 ....

E. I Cor. 13:4-7 ....

....

5. Define the following terms:
A. Teach ....

....

B. Instruct ....

....

....

C. Train ....

....

....

D. Discipline ....

....

....

E. Nurture ....

....

....

6. What does Psalm 127:3 teach us concerning our responsibility? ....

....

....

7. What are children like?
A. I Cor. 14:20 ....

B. I Cor. 3:1-3 ....

C. Mark 10:15 ....

8. A lack of security plagues the younger generation today. They are grasping for something stable, unmoveable, and real. From the following Scriptures, list some things we can do as a parent to help our children be secure:
A. Prov. 22:6 ....

....

B. Prov. 14:26 (Living) ....

....

C. II Cor. 1:17-19 (Living) ....

....

D. Matt. 18:10-14 ....

....

E. Prov. 3:11, 12 ....

....

9. What is the learning process?
   A. James 1:2-4 ....
   B. II Peter 1:12-15 ....
Note the spiral of learning: repetition, experience, relearning, experience and so forth. This should produce progressive change upward toward more complete understanding.
10. Where else do children learn apart from the home?
    A. Prov. 1:10-14 ....
    B. Ps. 119:105 ....
    C. John 14:26 ....
    D. I Sam. 12:23
11. Read Hebrews 12:5-11 in at least three translations. Then record what, to you, are the four most important aspects of this passage.
    A. ....
    B. ....
    C. ....
    D. ....

12. Match the following Scriptures with the principles involved regarding discipline:

PRINCIPLES		SCRIPTURES
Expression of love	....	Matt. 5:37
Don't nag	....	Prov. 13:24
Be consistent	....	Eccl. 5:5
Be fair	....	Gen. 37:3
Be impartial	....	James 1:8
Use an inanimate object	....	Acts 10:34
Fulfill every promise	....	Prov. 23:13, 14
Don't lose your temper	....	Prov. 25:28
Get the facts	....	Prov. 18:13
Do it now	....	Eccl. 8:11

13. What can be the result of undisciplined children?
    A. I Sam. 3:13 ....
    B. Titus 1:16, I Tim. 3:4 ....

    ....
    C. Prov. 29:15 ....

    ....
    D. Prov. 19:18 (Living) "Discipline your son in his early years while there is hope. If you don't you will ruin his life." ....

    ....
    ....

Proper discipline is a crying need of every child.

14. What are some of the reasons mothers do not discipline their children? ....
....
....
....
....
....

15. Children also need encouragement. Match the ways of encouragement with the following Scriptures:

    WAYS   SCRIPTURES
    Be kind and understanding   .... James 1:19
    Listen to them   .... Prov. 31:26
    Take time for them   .... Eccl. 3:1
    Take time with them   .... John 21:3-6
    Be interested in their interests .... Mark 3:14
    Show your love and approval   .... 1 Jn. 3:18

16. In what ways have your children been a spiritual blessing to you? ....
....
....

17. From the following examples from the Word of God, what would you say is one of the greatest influences in forming a child's character? John 4:53, Job 1:5, Mark 5:22-24, 41, 42 ....
....
....

18. Write in these columns what you feel your strengths and weaknesses are as a parent.

    STRENGTHS   WEAKNESSES

PRACTICAL HELPS

A. Life of the parents

1) We can't make Christ a reality to them if He is not to us. II Tim. 1:5
2) Practice what you want them to practice. I Cor. 11:1
   a. Disciples are followers. Children follow and imitate us; we're making disciples after our own pattern of living. Phil. 4:9
   b. If we want them to have our characteristics, have them around. Mark 3:14a
3) Pray for wisdom. James 1:5
4) Mom and Dad TOGETHER in discipline. Ps. 133:1
5) Encourage and support one another regarding the children. Deut. 3:28a
6) Don't be touchy or over-protective regarding the children. Prov. 28:25a
7) Prayer—keep the children committed. I Sam. 1:27, 28
8) Watch parental pride. It is easy to require too much when we want to make an impression. Phil. 2:3, 4

B. Encouragement

1) Be tolerant and understanding. Prov. 31:26
2) Be a good listener. Give your undivided attention. James 1:19
3) Take time for them. Your presence means everything. Eccl. 3:1
4) Plan family activities. .
5) Consider them in family decisions.
6) Be interested in their interests. Illus. John 21:3-6
7) Be vocal in expressions of love. Let them know you love them and look for ways to show love. I Jn. 3:18

C. Discipline or training

1) Discipline only in the principles. (i.e. disobedience, dishonesty, disrespect, untruthfulness, etc.) Prov. 29:17
2) Discipline FIRMLY but NOT in temper. Col. 3:21
3) Set realistic standards and requirements. Amos 7:7

a. Not too high. Don't expect too much; it results in trouble. Superimposed spirituality now means carnality later. Matt. 15:8
b. Plan to keep them. Prov. 13:19
c. Let children know what is expected. Be sure it is clear. Prov. 22:6
d. Be consistent. James 1:6
e. Avoid "if you do that again" syndrome.
f. Don't expose them to public ridicule.
g. Don't indulge them.
h. Be willing to apologize when needed.
i. Don't nag.
5) Get children to help. I Sam. 16:11
6) The greatest thing parents can do for their children is to love one another.

Suggestions For Further Study

Tape 1150AB — "Child Rearing I"
Tape 1151AB — "Child Rearing II"
Tape 1152AB — "Child Rearing III"
Tape 971A — "Disciplining"
Tape 971B — "Restricting"
Tape 26 — "Parent-Child Relationship"
Tape 1064 — "Spiritual Goals for the Child"
Tape 1065 — "The Child's Two Needs; Love & Discipline"
Tape 1807 & 1808 — "Priesthood of Parents"
Tape 1811 & 1812 — "God's Order for Parents"
Tape 1965 — "God's Order for Children"
Parents on the Run by Willard & Marguerite Beecher, Julian Press
Dare to Discipline by James Dobson, Tyndale House
Children, Fun or Frenzy by Mr. and Mrs. Al Fabrizio, Box 182, Palo Alto, California
Heaven Help the Home, by Howard Hendricks, Victor Press
Understanding Your Children, by Dr. Clyde Narramore, Zondervan publishers.